How to Feel Differently about Food

For my mother and father, in memoriam, and to my brother Clive. I wish I had known then what I know now about food and how best to mitigate the risks of our particular genetic Russian roulette by choosing to nourish our minds and bodies with real food. Be well, Nig. I love you. *Sally*

For my wonderful parents Pat and Joy. They really believed the food they ate was healthy when in fact it was anything but. They both passed away far too early in very poor health, leaving me to wonder if I'd known then what I know now, how much longer they could have lived and how much richer their lives might have been. *Liz*

How to Feel Differently about Food

Liberation and recovery from emotional eating

Sally Baker & Liz Hogon

With nutritional guidance from
Eve Gilmore

and a Foreword by
Dr Matthew S Capehorn

Hammersmith Health Books
London, UK

First published in 2017 by Hammersmith Health Books – an imprint of
Hammersmith Books Limited
4/4A Bloomsbury Square, London WC1A 2RP, UK
www.hammersmithbooks.co.uk

Disclaimer: The information in this book is of a general nature and is meant for educational purposes only. It is not intended as medical advice. The contents may not be used to treat, or diagnose, any particular disease or any particular person. Applying elements from this publication does not constitute a professional relationship or professional advice or services. No endorsement or warranty is explicitly given or implied by any entity connected to this content.

Note: Neither Sally Baker nor Liz Hogon is a trained dietitian. They have, however, studied and researched over many years the latest thinking about food and nutrition and its relationship to their therapeutic work. They have also worked successfully with hundreds of clients to help them to feel differently about food and take their first steps to liberation and recovery from emotional eating.
As always, if you are have pre-existing health issues and especially if you are taking any medications, you are advised first to consult your health practitioner before making any changes to your eating regime.

British Library Cataloguing in Publication Data: a CIP record of this book is available from the British Library.

Print ISBN: 978-1-78161-094-7
Ebook ISBN: 978-1-78161-095-4

Special thanks to Rachel Neylin
Editor: Georgina Bentliff
Cover and illustrations: Annie Rickard Straus
Test designed and typeset by: Julie Bennett of Bespoke Publishing Ltd
Index: Dr Laurence Errington
Production: Helen Whitehorn of Path Projects Ltd
Printed and bound by: TJ International Ltd

Contents

Preface

We would like to express our gratitude to the many clients we have worked with over the years. They have often battled with long-term shame and secrecy around their eating habits and this has led to all manner of disordered eating behaviours, from bingeing to compulsive eating, emotional eating or food addiction, all of which significantly affect a person's mental, physical and emotional wellbeing.

Many of our clients were already expert dieters when they came to us, having tried every diet from Atkins to the Zone, and they often felt their inability to lose weight and keep it off was their own fault. The yo-yo dieting pattern experienced by so many – that of losing weight only to regain it again – reinforced their feelings of failure. In turn, the hunger pangs they experienced following restrictive, low-fat diets inevitably triggered their most vulnerable emotions around food and often prompted them to eat all the more.

Our new book, *How to Feel Differently about Food*, is for those who recognise they have a challenging relationship with food. It explains that it is diets that fail people, not people who fail at diets. The statistics are well documented and show that up to 99 per cent of weight-reducing diets fail to produce permanent weight loss and that 75 per cent of dieters regain the weight they lost within 12 months (Mann, 2007).

It also questions the propaganda of the 40-billion-dollar diet industry that espouses low-fat foods and calorie-controlled diet programmes together with the pharmaceutical industry's slimming drugs whose business model requires failure for their own ongoing growth. If how you *feel* about food remains dysfunctional – and starving yourself of vital nutrients is unlikely to improve this – you will not achieve change.

The book goes further and makes a clear case for a paradigm shift from eating primarily to lose weight to eating real food to promote both mental and physical wellbeing – recognising the influence food has on mood and motivation – and thereby achieve successful weight loss.

Sally Baker
Liz Hogon
January 2017

Foreword

With most medical conditions, as time goes on and further research is carried out, the picture becomes clearer, and how to treat those conditions becomes more straightforward. However, the best way to eat to achieve weight loss and optimum health seems to be the exception. A quick internet search of diets, and how to lose weight, demonstrates just how many opinions there are on what we should all be doing and eating. Perhaps this is a reflection of the fact that what works for one person does not work for another, and an individualised approach is needed. However, surely there should not be confusion over what constitutes a 'healthy' diet, as this should apply to everyone? Yet there has never been more diverse opinion on this matter.

In 2014, a significant systematic review and meta-analysis (by Chowdury et al) looked at a huge amount of available evidence to question our beliefs about dietary fat. Its conclusion was startling, in that the evidence did not support current cardiovascular guidelines on fat consumption. Could it be that for a generation, public health guidance on what we should be eating had been wrong? Of course there were some conclusions that were not disputable, such as fat is a calorie-dense macronutrient (9 kilocalories per gram) and as such, in excess, it can cause weight gain, which itself is one of the most important modifiable risk factors for heart disease. Also, there was agreement that 'trans fats', or partially hydrogenated oils from processed foods, are carcinogenic and harmful. But could we all go back to eating foods that are high in fat, so long as it is part of a calorie-controlled diet?

We know that each of the macronutrient food groups has a different effect on our gut hormones, and therefore our brain's interpretation of how full we are. Levels of the hunger hormone, ghrelin, stay lower for longer after a meal high in fat when compared with a meal high in carbohydrates, which contributes to why many individuals do well on a high-fat, low-carbohydrate, 'paleo'-style diet.

However, this has led many experts to focus on sugar as the true 'enemy' to successful weight loss and management. It is certainly true that, despite adding flavour to food, and being a good source of rapid energy, refined sugar has no nutritional value, and as such consists of 'empty' calories contributing to weight gain, and also to tooth decay. Most people agree that our consumption of refined sugar is too high. In 2015, the World Health Organisation (WHO) cut its recommended sugar intake for adults in half, from the original 10 per cent of our total daily intake of calories to six per cent (which for a typical, average weight adult would be 25 grams, or approximately six teaspoons per day). This was shortly followed by Public Health England guidelines agreeing that we should all aim for this same sugar reduction, quoting a current average consumption of between 12 and 15 per cent of total daily calories. In 2016, the UK Government announced that it would be introducing a sugar levy, initially aimed at soft drinks, in response to pressure from experts and high profile celebrities. However, is it fair to say that it is sugar consumption that has caused the obesity and diabetes epidemic?

In March 2016, the long-awaited update to the UK's 'Eatwell Plate', now re-named the 'Eatwell Guidelines', was published to mixed reviews. Not surprisingly, supporters of high-fat, low-carbohydrate diets were highly critical of its heavy focus on carbohydrates, and many suggested it was all too similar to the previous advice originally published in 2007. However, is this just a reflection of how limited the evidence base actually is? Until the evidence for change is overwhelming, it would be inappropriate to advise the public of anything else.

A recent opinion article, published as a document from the National Obesity Forum (NOF), recently added to the debate, and public confusion. Entitled 'Eat Fat, Cut Carbs, and Avoid Snacking to Reverse Obesity and Type 2 Diabetes', the authors (Malhotra et al, 2016) claimed that fat had been demonised for too long and that sugar was the real demon. Some of the claims made in the article reflected the current controversies in nutrition, but the article went further, stating that calories should be ignored and so long as a high-fat, low-carbohydrate diet was followed (aiming for zero per cent sugar intake) then obesity and type 2 diabetes would be 'cured'. Unfortunately, this resulted in a backlash from the scientific community, including Public Health England, Diabetes UK and the Association for the Study of Obesity – they said it did not reflect the current body of evidence, and this led to further unhelpful confusion for the public. It even provoked a backlash from the majority of the NOF Board members who also disagreed with some of the claims made in the article, and who had not been consulted about the contents or whether it could be published as an NOF document. Ultimately there were some well-publicised resignations.

Perhaps understandably, the public have never been more confused about what they should be eating.

Can one macronutrient really be to blame? And will reducing its consumption, perhaps even getting it down to zero, really result in a 'cure' for obesity? Regrettably we can still consume too many calories of everything else, and here lies one fundamental problem. Even if one food group is worse than another, either in terms of nutrition or its effect on our metabolism or in terms of inducing satiety, the bottom line is that if we eat too much, we put on weight. Nutritional health is very important, but whilst controversy surrounds the exact composition of the perfect diet, we should focus on controlling how much food we take in, and perhaps more importantly challenge the reasons why we often eat when we are not really hungry, and our underlying relationship with food.

In August of 2016, there was a momentous shift in how the medical profession sees the future of obesity management. The publication of the National Institute for Health and Care Excellence (NICE) Quality Standard for the Prevention and Lifestyle Weight Management Programmes for Obesity in Adults clearly defined a tiered and structured approach to obesity care. Most importantly it recognised the need to include 'talking therapies'; this marked an acceptance that psychological hunger is as powerful, and as important to tackle, as physiological hunger.

We can make anyone lose weight (lock them in a cupboard and don't feed them!) but, if we don't address the underlying reasons why they became overweight, they will face precisely the same psychological problems they had at the start, and are more likely to put the weight straight back on.

Most of us have experienced emotional eating – comfort eating or habit eating – and it's as responsible for weight gain as our metabolism and 'calories in, calories out'. Our relationship with food is complex, and not just physiological. We must overcome psychological hunger, and those occasions when we eat but are not really hungry. How many of us have paid for a meal in a restaurant and been full after the starter, but because we have paid for the meal we will override that feeling of fullness? Worse still, despite being very full when the dessert menu arrives, we ignore the signals from our stomach and order our favourite pudding.

Many of us experience this every evening at home. Our stomach is approximately the size of our two fists put together, but many of us will eat a main meal that is greater than this volume. If a meal is nutritionally balanced, we should feel full for six to eight hours, and yet, how many times do we get the 'munchies' a couple of hours later? This is not physiological hunger; it is psychological hunger, and we need to address this relationship with food to break these habits.

We are not going one day to be presented with a weight-loss drug that tackles psychological hunger, even if it can trick the brain into thinking we are full – too often we choose to override that feeling. It also explains why many people who have bariatric surgery, which they perceive as the solution to their weight problems, do not do very well and put any weight lost back on, and more.

Just as an alcoholic doesn't drink because he or she is thirsty, an overweight person doesn't overeat because of hunger. People in this situation eat for emotional reasons – a bad day at the office, a row with their partner, money worries or a relationship breakdown, along with boredom and easy availability – and food becomes their friend. 'Talking therapies' address these issues and are at last becoming accepted as a frontline treatment, just as they are in alcoholism and smoking.

Addressing our emotional eating is key to successful weight loss and essential for behaviour change that will prevent weight regain.

Therapists Sally Baker and Liz Hogon use their experience of working with hundreds of clients who have struggled with their relationship with food and take a fascinating and in-depth look at *how* to feel differently about food – one meal at a time. They explain in simple steps how the cycle of dieting and restrictive eating can be broken and how individuals can improve their chances for successful and sustained weight loss and improved wellbeing by eating for nourishment instead of self-deprivation.

Dr Matthew S Capehorn
Clinical Manager
Rotherham Institute for Obesity (RIO), UK

References

Chowdhury R, Warnakula S, Kunutsor S, et al (2014) Association of dietary, circulating, and supplement fatty acids with coronary risk: a systematic review and meta-analysis. *Annals of Internal Medicine* 160(6): 398-406. DOI: 10.7326/M13-1788.

Malhotra A, Haslam D, Feltham S, Unwin D, Chandaria S, Fung J, DiNicolantonio J, Deakin T, Zinn C, Brukner P (2016) Eat Fat, Cut Carbs, and Avoid Snacking To Reverse Obesity and Type 2 Diabetes. National Obesity Forum and Public Health Collaboration. http://www.nationalobesityforum. org.uk/index.php/136-news_/746-%E2%80%9Ceat-fat,-cut-the-carbs-and-avoid-snacking-to-reverse-obesity-and-type-2-diabetes-%E2%80%9D.html (Accessed 19 September 2016)

National Institute for Health and Care Excellence (NICE) (2016) Obesity in adults: preobesity in adults: prevention and lifestyle weight management programmes: Quality standard QS111. nice.org.uk/guidance/qs111 (Accessed 19 September 2016)

About the authors and how we came to write this book

We are two therapists based on opposite sides of the planet (Sally in London, England; Liz in Melbourne, Australia). Although we couldn't be geographically further apart this has not always been the case and our friendship and our professional collaboration began over 16 years ago in London, the city we shared for almost a decade.

As therapists with our own busy practices we have a specific interest in working with people struggling with their relationship with food. Our professional collaboration resulted in us creating a new combined therapy approach that we have made our own. It is informed by the years we have spent building up our knowledge and learning the necessary insights to discover the often subconscious reasons for comfort- and stress-eating, sugar cravings and self-sabotaging behaviour around food. This culminated in us co-writing our first book, *Seven Simple Steps to Stop Emotional Eating* published in 2015 by Hammersmith Books, London, UK.

Why this new book?

The therapy we undertake with our emotional eating clients is some of the most rewarding and satisfying work we do. Working with them to resolve their uncomfortable issues and self-sabotaging behaviours around food means they are able to achieve sustainable weight loss, often after many years of disordered eating, including bingeing, compulsive sugar cravings and assorted other entrenched and unhelpful eating habits. Losing weight can be life-changing and have a hugely positive effect on existing medical conditions and future health prospects. It also manifests with heightened feelings of self-esteem and a personal sense of empowerment after years of unsuccessful yo-yo dieting and the associated shame and guilt.

Working in the field of emotional eating, we became fascinated by the growing body of scientific research linking poor nutritional choices – driven by the desire to lose weight – to an increased incidence of depression. We knew how vulnerable emotional eaters were to the latest diet industry quick-fix or shiny packaged detox with its promise of effortless weight loss. We also knew how a month or two of intensive food restriction or newbie enthusiasm at the gym rarely adds up to making authentic, lasting changes in body shape or size but can detrimentally affect how people feel about themselves.

Eventually it became imperative for us to put together all the key aspects we had learnt over the years about nutrition, weight loss and enhanced wellbeing to create this book. As you do begin to feel differently about food you will find you are then able to make the changes, adjustments and improvements to what and how you eat, that can break the dieting cycle once and for all. With this change in thinking comes the shift from an unnatural and unhelpful pattern of restrictive eating purely for weight loss to one of eating for optimum health and wellbeing.

What we advocate in *How to Feel Differently about Food* is not a diet. Through our work it became clear that eating purely for weight loss – what is generally meant by 'dieting' – is not the best way of taking care of yourself and is usually not sustainable. It is ultimately at odds with how people were designed to eat and thrive.

Sally Baker

I am a therapist, speaker and writer and have been working for more than a decade in London. I see clients both face to face, and remotely the world over by Skype, for a wide range of issues. My specialism is helping clients to resolve their self-sabotaging behaviour in whatever form it shows up in their life and to resolve and release limiting beliefs that inhibit them living to their full potential. I am particularly interested in how anxiety can lead to binge eating, sugar cravings and emotional eating. I work with clients to explore and release long-held patterns of behaviour so that they can improve their physical and mental wellbeing and achieve and maintain a healthy weight.

The experience of working in my own private practice, and the close collaboration I enjoy with Liz Hogon, formed the basis and inspiration for our self-help book, *Seven Simple Steps to Stop Emotional Eating*. (Hammersmith Books, 2015).

How to Feel Differently about Food came again from the close collaboration with Liz Hogon. We wanted to show how eating a restrictive diet solely aimed at losing weight is punishing for your body and is not the best way either to take care of yourself or to achieve your weight-loss goal. We set out to provide a straightforward guide to eating real food for people who want to optimise their physical and mental health, and to shed excess weight if appropriate, while at the same time juggling the demands of a busy life.

Many of our clients have had a destructive relationship with food for many years. We concluded that with so much disinformation and conflicting nutritional advice in the media about what people should, and should not, eat, many people are confused when trying to make healthy-eating decisions for themselves. This is especially true for people who have had little or no experience of healthy eating in the past or who feel they don't know where to start when making improvements to their eating choices.

Although not a trained dietician, I have read widely about nutrition and have over the past decade become disillusioned with much of the nutritional information produced for the public by influential organisations, including the UK's own National Health Service (NHS) and its latest public health information, *The Eatwell Guide* [http://www.nhs.uk/Livewell/Goodfood/Pages/the-eatwell-guide.aspx; alternatively here is the bitly link http://bit.ly/1rioo1g]. Purporting to guide the public to achieve a balance of healthier and more sustainable food choices, it ignores the latest medical opinion linking low-fat products and vegetable oils and spreads, with compromised health outcomes and higher obesity figures while actively promoting simple carbohydrates by including crisps, biscuits and ice cream in its guidance.

I have found that a great deal of the health information produced for the general public originates from companies with vested interests in maintaining the status quo. I have also been disappointed that scientific research almost exclusively concentrates on drug-based interventions for chronic disease. The benefits of enhancing physical and mental health that can be achieved by eating natural foods are often ignored by institutions and organisations; I have to assume this is because there is little or no money to be made from promoting the benefits of eating real food.

Liz Hogon

I qualified as a full-time therapist in 2001. Since then I have helped thousands of people with hypnotherapy and other key therapeutic approaches to stop emotional eating, cease smoking and end phobias, as well as treating a range of issues relating to anxiety and depression.

I became interested in alternative therapies and nutrition when I failed to recover from a severe bout of Ross River fever. This debilitating mosquito-borne virus attacks the immune system and left me exhausted, with no medical resolution. As well as using the power of visualisation, and other powerful therapy approaches to support my body's recovery, I began exploring the role of nutrition in promoting increased wellbeing. I started to search beyond the basic nutrition guidelines recommended by my doctors and began a life-time interest in eating for enhanced physical and emotional wellbeing.

My learning process has been by trial and error; and finding my own way of eating that best suited me has meant learning the useful skill of listening to my own body and increasing my intuition. In hectic phases of my life, I can tell, by my muscle aches and joint pains, stress headaches and disturbed sleep, if my eating has slipped from the optimum. Equally, I have learnt how to pull my nutrition back around to what my body really needs, and time and time again this has meant reducing simple carbohydrates and avoiding sugary and refined foods to eat some good quality protein with a wide variety of vegetables and greens. In essence, it is eating the good, wholesome food of my youth with the addition of some basic paleo guidelines that really works for me; not only can I tell the difference in my waist measurement, but more importantly in my general wellbeing.

As a therapist working with weight-loss clients, I became frustrated for my clients who were determined to lose weight, submitted themselves to starvation diets or following fad 'celebrity' diets, and were left feeling constantly hungry and often depressed. It became pressing for me to be able to provide an alternative to the propaganda pushed by the diet and slimming industry, to suggest eating guidelines that would encourage weight loss while providing nourishment for a healthy body and mind.

I had worked with Sally, leading therapy workshops in London, and we collaborated professionally while I was based in the UK. We then continued to work together by Skype to co-write *Seven Simple Steps to Stop Emotional Eating*, published by Hammersmith Books in 2015. Now settled back in my native Australia, I have made my home in Melbourne, and work full-time in my own busy private practice.

I now feel the missing piece of the jigsaw is finally in place. Sally and I have not only created our own unique approach to ending disordered eating but we are now in a position to support people's nutritional choices as they successfully bring their body and mind into balance with a healthy-eating plan for life.

About the Nutritional Advisor

Eve Gilmore is a naturopath, clinical nutritionist, homeopath, CST (Craniosacral Therapy) and CEASE (Complete Elimination of Autistic Spectrum Expression) practitioner who has been researching the links between diet and specific health problems for more than 20 years while working in private practice with patients with complex long-term conditions and achieving major successes for them. She is a writer and speaker on health and also runs training courses on natural medicine for health professionals.

Key principles of how to feel differently about food

An increasing number of people recognise that how they feel about food has little in common with the simple and natural life-affirming act of eating for nourishment. For some people, just thinking about food can make them feel uncomfortable, anxious or stressed. For them, their body's need for food is an inconvenience. It is something to be minimised at best and over-indulged at worst. Their appetite comes at the cost of a daily fear of gaining weight. This fear drives their constant over-thinking about food coupled with feeling fraught about every meal choice they make as they regret each mouthful of food that they swallow.

How they feel about food has developed, sometimes over many years, into something complex and self-destructive and utterly at odds with their general health and wellbeing. It is not surprising that treating one's appetite as the enemy inhibits nature's desire for the whole person to achieve balance and to thrive.

These negative feelings are the judgemental and self-critical thoughts emotional eaters live with every day. Emotional eaters often construct self-damaging habits around food which can have increasingly negative effects, on both their physical and mental wellbeing, contributing to increased levels of anxiety and lowered self-esteem, and even leading to depression.

Typical emotional eaters experience years of yo-yo dieting, often accompanied by bouts of bingeing, compulsive sugar cravings, over-thinking about food, zoned out eating and even secret purging.

The focus on calorie restriction or low-fat diets coupled with the standalone desire to lose weight is the default setting for many emotional eaters. It is an approach doomed to failure. Statistics recently released by the Midland Community Health Council in Michigan confirmed that in the US one out of three women and one out of four men are on a diet at any given time. Even with all those commitments to weight loss, two-thirds of dieters regain any weight they lost within a year, many more within five years.

The global market for weight loss products was around $6 billion in 2015 according to an IBISWorld report (NAICS, 2016); the UK market alone is valued at £2 billion per year. The commercial model requires repeat customers so it is not surprising that weight loss disappointments far outnumber weight loss success stories however much money is spent on gym memberships, supplements, special foods and the like. Weight loss companies need a proportion of their customer base to fail and they have a commercial interest in them returning time and again either to join slimming clubs or to buy the latest diet product.

Emotional eating and fad diets are often two sides of the same coin. Advertisers understand how to manipulate emotional eaters with their tantalising quick-fix promises, knowing exactly how to trigger renewed weight loss optimism and spending. Their quest to reach the Holy Grail of being slimmer becomes all consuming, feeding into over-thinking and obsessive self-criticism. This self-perpetuating cycle of behaviour then vacillates between occasional weight loss success and inevitable weight gain. That in itself is dispiriting enough, and this behaviour can easily and disastrously slip into disordered eating.

Repetitive yo-yo dieting causes emotional eaters to lose touch with their own natural hunger so that they are not sure when they have eaten enough or are sated. Their body can become out of balance as a by-product of sugar cravings, carb binges and purging sessions. Equally, they are often at a loss as to how even to approach eating more healthily, as well as how to pursue their own wellness and fitness goals.

How to Feel Differently about Food sets out to explain in simple steps how the exhausting cycle of emotional eating can be broken and how it is possible to find liberation from the tyranny of over-thinking about food. It details how, because emotional eaters feel differently about food, they need their own unique recovery approach to find their way through the nutritional maze towards their goal of a healthy weight, with a healthy mind, in a healthy body.

Spotting the signs of emotional eating

For many who are compulsively driven to eat for emotional reasons, not hunger, food has become a manifestation of self-loathing and a complex method of self-harming, or even a way of failing to thrive. These people crave food, avoid food, binge on food and obsess about food. Thinking about food fills their every waking moment. Food has become a way to celebrate and commiserate with themselves. In fact, it is their everything – except a natural way to sate hunger or be a source of healthy nourishment.

Typically, emotional eaters feel their appetite for food is out of their control and is counter to their heart's desire to be slimmer than they are. They feel their inability to resist their food cravings proves how worthless they are as they trade their dreams of being slimmer for swallowing down foods they consider to be 'bad' or 'forbidden'. They also often believe that the excess weight they carry is their own personal failing and visible proof for all to see that they are weak, inadequate or just plain greedy. The story they tell themselves continues with the common beliefs that if they were stronger, or had more will-power, or were simply just 'better people', then they would find it easy to manage their weight-versus-food-intake without the daily time-consuming over-thinking that they endure.

We, the authors, are both therapists working in our own private practices. We specialise in working with clients to resolve the emotional reasons that drive comfort- and stress-eating. We understand that although every client has his or her own unique set of circumstances and history, there are similarities in thinking and in the belief system that defines each emotional eater. For instance, emotional eaters judge themselves harshly and their self-talk – the quiet voice that everyone hears within their own mind – is particularly critical and unforgiving. We also understand that emotional eaters can be triggered to binge eat when experiencing negative or challenging emotions, such as loneliness, sadness or anger.

In our professional experience, we have found the disordered thinking around food that emotional eaters experience makes it particularly challenging to establish a nutritionally balanced way of eating that can be sustained for the long term. This is particularly true for those who are attempting to stabilise their weight after years, or possibly even decades, of yo-yo dieting.

Emotional eaters do not generally fare well following a type of diet that brings any of the following circumstances into play:

1. Diets that promote low-calorie eating to a level that induces hunger can quickly feel unendurable and trigger strong self-sabotaging behaviour.
2. Diets that rely on low-fat foods to restrict calorie consumption can increase the occurrence or severity of low moods, even to the risk of increasing the incidence of depression.
3. Diets that replace foods containing real sugars with chemical sweeteners can still spark compulsive sugar cravings and out-of-control bingeing.
4. Diets that replace meals with fake-foods, such as shakes, snack bars, instant soups or variations on this theme, often fail for emotional eaters when they are challenged with the inevitable reintroduction of real food.
5. Diets that promote or exclude whole groups of food, impose excessive or irrational rules or demand a specific cooking methodology can all help encourage unhelpful over-thinking about food that emotional eaters are already prone to. This includes the eating of only 'free-from' foods, including gluten-free (without a confirmed medical need), or following a strict macrobiotic diet, or eating only raw foods.

In this book, we outline a unique way for emotional eaters to relearn, or perhaps to learn for the first time, what their body needs to thrive. Our approach takes the focus off pure weight loss to introduce and promote good health and improved mental wellbeing by eating real food. We have found this methodology works particularly well for those who have struggled in the past with emotional issues around food – for instance, if someone has experienced food scarcity as a child and has memories of hunger, or experienced disordered eating at any time in their life. By taking the focus primarily off weight loss and encouraging a holistic, whole-body approach, it is possible to show how real food with a high level of nutrition promotes satiety and stabilises mood.

From this well-nourished position many things become possible, including improved self-image, enhanced feelings of wellbeing and even motivation to move more, so that successful weight loss becomes a natural outcome of eating meals that are tasty, easy to prepare and satisfying.

Emotional eaters in particular struggle to maintain a healthy weight and establish a nutritionally balanced way of eating that can be sustained for the long term. We have been motivated by our extensive work with clients who identify as emotional eaters, to augment our therapeutic approach with the practical guidance found in this book, to help them establish healthy eating in their own lives.

Over time, our nutritional research has shaped key elements of *How to Feel Differently about Food*. This is *not* a diet book. We absolutely refuse to call eating real food a 'diet', as we believe this is the most natural way to eat at all times. It is also how we would have been eating had we not lost our way and become confused about which foods are good for us and which are not so good. We can thank the food manufacturing conglomerates and the agri-chemical industry that have comprehensively denatured our foods in the last 50 years or so, for the ongoing confusion.

In this book, we guide you in using nutrition for your greater good and we provide the information you need to take those important steps on your move away from food as a weapon of self-punishment to food as an expression of your will to thrive and be as healthy and happy as you can be.

A healthy weight versus a healthy person

Being slim is not a guarantee of being healthy. Thin people are no more immune to illness or chronic disease than those who are considered over-weight. In fact, there are many people who would be visually assessed to be at a healthy weight who achieve this by adhering to some very unhealthy and often secret eating habits.

There is also the acronym 'TOFI' (thin outside, fat inside) that describes how some slim people can look misleadingly more healthy than they really are.

The team of Professor Jimmy Bell based at Imperial College, London, has used MRI (magnetic resonance imaging) scans to reveal how much internal fat people who would be considered slim invisibly carry, surrounding their internal organs (Thomas et al, 2013). Professor Bell has spent years studying how human beings store and use their adipose tissue – that is, body fat. Thanks to using MRI, he and his team have shown that appearances can be very misleading. He said, 'We understand that fat infiltration of the liver can be linked to many serious health problems...' but, 'A diagnosis could easily be overlooked, especially with men who have a slim build but do little or no exercise.'

TOFIs would be wise to use this technological advance to make radical lifestyle changes as their fat is lying around their vital organs and is shown on the MRI scans to be streaked through their under-used muscles. It is this fat, far more than the dimpled subcutaneous fat lying under the skin, that sends out chemical signals which will eventually lead to insulin resistance, type 2 diabetes and heart disease.

The *Journal of the American Medical Association* featured scientific research using predefined BMI (Body Mass Index – see the box on page 7 opposite) categories correlated with mortality rates. The meta-analysis of over 40 separate studies showed that those in the BMI category designated as 'overweight' have the longest life expectancy while the majority of people who fall into the initial BMI obesity category (25.0 to 29.9) have the same lifespan as those in the normal BMI category (18.5 to 24.9). The research showed that carrying extra weight is only a real health issue in the case of weight levels higher than the BMI obesity category (30.0 to 39.9). Even though this is the case, many people jeopardise their health by trying to reduce their weight by eating less most of the time (Flegal et al, 2013).

There are more accurate benchmarks of health than the amount of fat one carries and yet people who are overweight are often the target for messages of doom from the medical profession. This targeting can be seen as an attempt to scare people into a renewed effort to slim down. It also contributes to society's enthusiasm for fat shaming. Whether driven by fear or shame, many overweight people decide to deprive themselves of food in a bid to lose weight and thereby perpetuate an unhealthy expression of how they relate to themselves and food.

It is acknowledged that the media's idealised representation of thin women makes many young women in particular feel dissatisfied with their own bodies. This is also prevalent for many new mothers who can feel under immense pressure to return to their pre-baby body size within the shortest possible time. This pressure coincides with a particularly vulnerable time for many new mothers who, instead of being supported to recuperate and enjoy this special time in their lives, are being judged negatively for their weight or body shape. The message is more pernicious than just vanity; it contributes to feelings of dissociation from themselves and can be a factor in postnatal depression. The last thing new mothers need is to feel pressured to under-eat or eat primarily with weight loss in mind. This will inevitably involve cutting down on foods that support their mental wellbeing and delay their full physical recovery.

Body Mass Index (BMI)

BMI as a measure of fat was developed over 150 years ago in Belgium. It is not applicable or appropriate for children, pregnant women, older people or anyone with a chronic illness. Equally, a very fit, muscular rugby player could easily have a BMI of 40 or greater putting him erroneously in the extremely obese category.

More recent medical opinion has moved away from using just BMI as a useful measure of weight and associated health risks. Researchers have discovered that a more accurate determinant of weight and health outcomes is *where* excess fat is carried on the body. It has been found that abdominal fat is the most potentially detrimental to health. The irony is that yo-yo dieting can encourage fat storage around the abdomen as repetitive cycling between restrictive food intake and unrestricted eating causes fat-storing enzymes to be increased in the body. When weight is lost and regained in this way it causes visceral

---

fat to be accumulated deep inside the abdomen area around all the organs in the belly leading to an increased risk of heart disease, insuline resistance and diabetes. This is further proof that dieting is antipathetic to good health.

BMI is assessed by taking your weight in kilos and dividing it by your height in metres squared. You do not have to be a maths genius to work out your own BMI as there are many free charts online that calculate the maths for you.

If your BMI is:

18.5 or less you are considered underweight;

18.5-24.9 you are considered normal weight;

25.0-29.9 you are considered overweight;

30.0-39.9 you are considered obese;

40 or greater you are considered extremely or 'morbidly' obese.

Reference: Flegal et al, 2013.

Why diets fail you

Nowhere is hope over experience more prevalent than in the world of the multimillion-dollar diet industry.

There is a growing amount of evidence suggesting that for many people going on a diet which restricts what you eat as a way of achieving enduring weight loss does not work and is not sustainable in either the mid or long term.

If restrictive or calorie-controlled diets worked, then by now one 'super diet' would have emerged and it would work for everyone, but this is definitely not the case. Hundreds of diet books are published every year and no doubt this trend will continue.

Any diet that encourages you to eat fewer calories, or to radically cut out whole food groups, in order to achieve weight loss is scientifically flawed. Denying yourself food to the point of going hungry convinces your sub-conscious mind that you are living in a time of food shortage or famine and passes messages to your body to hold onto its fat as your mind is not sure for how long the food shortage will continue. As you can imagine, this is counter-productive to good health as the body feels under stress.

If you have dieted in the past, and most people have, your mind will have a 'memory' of experiencing those periods of reduced food intake. Periods of self-induced calorie reduction where you experience hunger pangs are very difficult to maintain and are often the trigger for a stint of bingeing or excessive eating. This is what is meant by 'yo-yo dieting'. Yo-yo dieting like this can negatively affect your metabolism, making it even harder in the future to regulate your weight. If you recognise you have a pattern of dieting and bingeing, then it is even more vital that when you commit to eating real food as part of nutritionally balanced meals that leave you satisfied, and that you do not go hungry, as this will quickly plunge your metabolism back into fat-storing mode.

A holistic, all-body approach to eating real food means that there is no advantage to going hungry or feeling deprived. This approach is diametrically opposed to the usual diet model. In *How to Feel Differently about Food*, we encourage a way of eating that promotes reassuring your mind that nutritious food is available to you and that your body is no longer under threat of impending food shortage. This reassurance enables habitual stress levels around food to be reduced and when the stress symptoms of emotional eating are reduced, your body reduces its production of cortisol – the stress hormone that can also inhibit weight loss. Feeling less stressed also ensures that the nourishment in the foods that are eaten becomes more 'bio-available' and advantageous. Later in the book we explain how stress shuts down many of the processes of digestion, leaving sufferers deprived of essential nutrition.

Our methodology promotes resetting your metabolism into fat-burning mode instead of fat-storing mode and this is achieved through selecting appetising and tasty foods that encourage satiety. In addition, this approach focuses on the effect of refined sugar as a key cause of weight gain. Sugar and simple carbohydrates are rapidly absorbed into your bloodstream and affect your body's production of insulin. Rapid spikes in blood sugar cause insulin levels to rise and take sugar out of the bloodstream and into storage in the liver, muscles and (if they are full) fat cells; the high glucose level is therefore followed by a rapid drop in blood glucose levels. This in itself can be the cause of sugar cravings and the trigger for compulsive eating. The cumulative effect of eating in ways that spike insulin production eventually leads to what is called 'insulin resistance'. This is a condition in which the cells of the body become unresponsive to increasingly high levels of insulin and this is a key predictor of diabetes.

The latest figures from the Centers for Disease Control (CDC, 2014) in the US show that almost 10 per cent of the US population has been diagnosed with diabetes. The equivalent figures from Diabetes UK (2015) show figures approaching 3.5 million in 2015 and all predictions expect these numbers to grow year upon year. In addition, many, many more people the world over have 'pre-diabetes' (also known as metabolic syndrome) and remain undiagnosed until their health deteriorates with associated serious health problems – heart, circulation, eyesight and kidney damage – that bring them to medical attention and the confirmation of type 2 diabetes. Going back to health risks associated with being overweight, the incidence of pre-diabetes and diabetes itself is higher in patients who are classed as obese.

There are two other important hormones found to affect a person's ability to manage his/her weight. The first is called leptin. It is made by fat cells and works to decrease appetite. This can become unbalanced in response to insulin resistance caused by spikes in blood sugar levels. Leptin is responsible for sending messages to your brain that you've eaten enough and feel sated. When leptin's signaling goes awry, the hormone stops being produced so the messages that you have eaten enough are no longer sent, which leads to an inability to determine satiety. This is called 'leptin resistance'. Medical professionals are now focusing more on the part leptin plays in the development of obesity, and how the hormone responds may actually be the result of obesity. The second key hormone involved with appetite is called ghrelin and its job is to signal to you that you are hungry. It also influences how quickly you feel hungry again after eating. Ghrelin naturally increases before meal times and is then designed to reduce after eating for around three hours until it once more naturally increases to signal the need to eat again. However, this hormone too can become unbalanced and send hunger signals more frequently, encouraging a reduction in the time between meals or even promoting the habit of constant grazing on food. One way that ghrelin becomes out of balance is through stress, which disturbs sleep patterns. This can affect workers who work unnatural hours such as night shifts. Not getting enough sleep has been shown to increase levels of ghrelin and cause an increase in appetite. (See The sleep cure on page 18.)

In simple terms, the hormonal responses that help manage appetite and weight are like a house of cards that are all interdependent on each other to maximise your health, weight management and wellbeing. Although designed to be perfectly in balance, a key element that can cause the whole house of cards to collapse is the eating of sugar and simple carbohydrates. It doesn't take long before sugar spikes begin to undermine the complex hormonal interactions.

The good news is that by reducing stress levels, improving sleep patterns and changing the types of food eaten it is possible to re-calibrate the hormones' signals to the brain to promote a feeling of fullness and enhanced wellbeing. On the food front this is achieved by cutting out refined sugars, simple carbohydrates and processed foods and replacing them with real foods, including plenty of good fats, such as olive oil, oily fish and nuts that your body can naturally process.

Nudging yourself towards change

The 'nudge theory' is about nudging or encouraging behavioural changes through positive reinforcement and indirect suggestion. In the wider world, nudge theory has been applied to economics, politics and health. Supporters of the effectiveness of the theory exist in the hallowed halls of academia, the

White House and in the British Government to name but a few. So, how can nudge theory be applied to you eating more healthily in your own life?

Your existing habits, thoughts and beliefs have brought you to where you are today, so nudging towards making positive changes is vital in allowing effortless changes and maintaining them into the future.

Decide when

In practical terms, this means choosing a time to initiate changes that has the most chance of success. It is surprising how many people set themselves up to fail by launching a new initiative without thinking through how much they already have to do in their life. This may mean scheduling changes to how you shop, eat and cook after a family holiday, or a big social event, such as a wedding or birthday party. Look at your diary for an opportunity when there may be a lull in stress levels at home or work, or a time when you are able to give more energy to embrace initial changes to your usual eating habits. If you are canny with your timing you will be giving yourself a head start towards success.

Ditch the crap

Behaving with your usual default habits around food perpetuates your feeling the same way about yourself. It is a truism that if you keep doing what you have always done you'll get the same results you've always got before. Reaching for snacks in your kitchen that you have always reached for maintains the status quo, so an important part of your preparation is to ditch the old low-nutrition, poor-quality processed foods in your cupboards and replace them with more tasty and nutritious options. If you're not the only family member using the kitchen, then separate out their foods from yours and claim space and ownership of the foods you want to eat. Ideally, your efforts to maximise your health and wellbeing would be supported by all family members, but more often than not you will face resistance. If you wait for everyone in your life to come on-board you could wait a life time, so do as Mahatma Gandhi suggested: 'Be the change you want to see.' Set your own standard and let those who challenge you see how much healthier and happier you are. It's about doing something for yourself. (Of course, you may find others are challenged and discomforted by a healthier, happier you – they will not admit that what you have done is a good thing and will, possibly unconsciously, try to undermine it. Be alert to this; don't respond but just recognise their fear of change and continue with your own positive work.)

Just because you've decided to nudge yourself towards better nutrition doesn't mean you will magic away all your impulses to snack. This is especially true while you are adjusting to this new way of eating and feeling about food. The nudge ensures everything you need is at hand to fulfil your mealtime and snacking requirements to maximise your nutrition. This may mean shopping differently and stocking your cupboards and fridge with different foods. You will find a comprehensive list of real foods in the 'Foods to embrace and enjoy' section later in the book on page 69.

The hunger trap

Do you skip breakfast and feel ravenous around 11 am? Do you skip lunch or eat a high-fat, high-carb, high-sugar lunch, such as pasta or pizza, that leaves you a couple of hours later desperate for something to eat to counter your mid-afternoon energy slump? Do you get home after work and immediately start hoovering up everything you could eat by the light of the fridge?

Eating when you are too hungry makes it challenging to be discerning about food. It contributes to setting you up to fail. It's a similar experience to shopping when overly hungry as your empty belly can adversely affect your food choices. You can find your intentions to buy healthier food thwarted as you are drawn to the baked goods aisle or to putting questionable quality processed foods into your basket. (Research shows that shopping when you are hungry increases what you buy overall, including making random purchases such as batteries that you do not really need and did not have on your shopping list.)

Noticeable spikes in your hunger levels are an indicator that you are under-nourished for at least parts of the day. Completing the food and mood diary available as a free pdf download (see below) will help to highlight where your nutritional deficits originate. You may find your mood and appetite feel much more balanced on days when you eat a protein-based breakfast, like eggs, instead of a cereal-based breakfast, or when you have a healthy-sized portion of meat, fish or cheese with salad at lunch time instead of grabbing a sandwich. You will also gain insights into the type of foods that leave you feeling satisfied and energised for several hours compared with those that leave you feeling bloated and sluggish. Use the food and mood diary (see page 133) to nudge the creation of your own eating plan to develop new eating habits that support your energy levels throughout your busy day. We give you many ideas for snacks and meals that could prove to be more beneficial for you in the 'Foods to embrace and enjoy' section of the book on page 69.

Footnote: To download the A4-printer-friendly PDF version of the Food and Mood Diary template, go to www.feeldifferently.co.uk and click on Therapy Tools see Worksheets tab.

Creating new rituals and habits

Everyone has their own set of habits and rituals, many of which originate in childhood. It is estimated that 40 per cent of the things we do every day actually happen in a zoned-out way, without us needing to give them a great deal of thought or effort. In terms of mental efficiency, how our mind handles our recurring habits frees up our thinking to devote mental energy to more innovative tasks. This is why the embedded habits you want to change can be so challenging.

It is your habits and rituals that have brought you to where you are today and the prospect of creating positive changes and feeling differently about food will mean it is time to replace some of those old habits that do not serve you with new ones that can support the changes you want to see in your life. It is easier for your mind to adopt new habits than it is to let go of existing ones, so it would help you to use 'scaffolding techniques' to do this. 'Scaffolding' in this context is not about buildings per se but it is about construction. In education, scaffolding is a term used to introduce fresh concepts in a way that builds new information onto existing knowledge, and the new information can feel firmly embedded as it is built on solid foundations of learning.

So, in the context of how to feel differently about food, you can choose any aspect of your eating and use scaffolding to create a new ritual. Examples of some habits that people have often told us they would like to change are:
- eating meals in a distracted or zoned-out way;
- rushing to leave the house without the time to eat a nutritious breakfast; or
- the growing phenomenon of linking eating with the viewing or streaming of a whole TV series in a single sitting. (We explore this habit more fully next.)

Binge TV and eating

There is a well-recognised link between the number of hours of television viewing per week and weight gain. It was stated in the US National Weight Loss Registry that most people are able to lose weight and maintain their weight loss if they view less than 10 hours of TV per week. However, the average American is reported as viewing nearly 40 hours of television each week.

Add in to those viewing hours the popular leisure activity of watching a whole series of your favourite TV show in one sitting and the hours become almost unimaginably inflated.

The habit here is not just one of inactivity; watching television is often accompanied with mindless eating, or distracted eating, of all sorts of sugary or high-salt, high-carb and high-fat snacks.

The ideal health-promoting change would be to separate all eating from watching TV and ultimately reduce the number of hours spent on the sofa. However, we acknowledge how challenging changing habits is, and recommend using scaffolding techniques to help you to successfully achieve the changes you want.

The scaffolding you could put into place would be the steps to take to ensure the greatest level of success for enduring change.

For example:

1. You can no longer just reach for your same old binge snack foods if you have removed them from your home. If that is not possible, then put them somewhere inconvenient. If you live with someone else, let them know you are making changes to how you eat and ask them for their help by being considerate in their behaviour.

2. Restock the same place where once the unhealthy foods were stored with healthier snack alternatives. Don't forget to include alternatives to your usual fizzy drinks. That means replacing zero-calorie, sugar-free brands too. (You can read more about swapping snacks for healthier choices in snack food on page 106.)

3. Eat a scheduled meal before settling down to binge view TV. Encourage yourself to eat your meals away from the television or other electronic distractions. Serve all the food you intend to eat on a plate, preferably at the table. This focus helps your body and mind to get maximum satisfaction from your meals. You also get to recognise what you are eating and are aware of quantity, variety and quality.

4. Treat sitting on the sofa for hours on end as a similar health risk to a long-haul flight. In fact some doctors are recognising prolonged sitting can be as serious a health risk as smoking cigarettes. There is an acknowledged connection between viewing television for more than five hours per evening and a future diabetes diagnosis. Set an alarm or timer to remind you to get up at regular intervals to move around and stretch.

5. Make a note of your viewing habits for at least a week. You may be surprised how much of your leisure time is devoted to just watching television. Use this knowledge to make adjustments and add more structure to your precious recreation time.

6. Zoned-out behaviour around binge viewing and binge eating can be a symptom of spending too much time alone or under-stimulated.

Consider what else you could add into your evening or weekend. Listening to music, reading a book, or playing a video game are all pretty sedentary but can begin to help you break the hold of mindless TV and, who knows, the right music could lead to spontaneous living room dancing, while working out at home to an exercise DVD could provide the impetus for joining a regular class. Also, telephoning a friend for a chat or inviting them around for a few hours could change this passive mode enough for you to consider going out for a coffee or taking a walk.

This way of scaffolding changes to your habits is just an example and you can customise your own scaffolding to create new habits and rituals wherever you want to see changes around food, in any part of your life. The same approach can be used to scaffold your eating rituals around going to the cinema, for instance. The outcome might be to change your usual order of large popcorn and large soda pop into a pre-screening healthy meal, or by taking with you your own chopped-up fruit and nuts with a natural fruit-flavoured soda water. How much scaffolding would you need to implement that change?

Mindful eating

So many people eat nowadays while driving, surfing the net, watching television, standing at an open fridge or strolling along the road. They treat eating like listening to the radio – something to do while doing something else.

Over the last few years there has been an increase in the blurring between meal times and an almost constant grazing and snacking, with fast food outlets on every high street.

In the workplace a culture has developed where employees are only excused from their desk if they are smokers and are outside having a cigarette. There is an unspoken expectation in many offices that staff eat their lunch while remaining at their workstations, often eating while they continue to work.

Eating food has almost become an unconscious activity that happens while you are doing other things.

These habits are counter productive to health, wellbeing and most likely productivity too; even machines benefit from having some down time. Feeling differently about food is not just about *what* you choose to eat but *how* you eat your meals.

We suggest you eat three meals a day, starting with breakfast if you have an appetite for it, plus a small mid-morning and mid-afternoon snack if you feel you require it.

The routine of regular meal times helps to encourage your body to go into fat-burning mode by reassuring your body that food is plentiful and regularly available so that your body does not need to store fat. Regular meals help to reverse the harm you may have done to your metabolism by years of yo-yo dieting when your body never knew whether you were about to impose a period of feasting or fasting.

When you do eat, put your food onto a plate. Turn the TV off or move away from your computer. Pull up a chair and sit down at a table.

Focus on your food; after all, this is your opportunity to provide yourself with the best quality nutrition you can source at that time. It is an opportunity to take the best care of yourself.

The key to mindful eating is to really enjoy your food, relishing every mouthful as you eat. Chew your food well, and if your mouth is full your hands should be empty. This is a useful way of slowing down your eating so that your brain gets the message from your stomach that it is full and that you have had enough to eat.

The sleep cure

Do you struggle to fall asleep at night with your mind racing ten-to-the-dozen?

Do you fall immediately asleep when your head hits the pillow only to have your eyes spring open determinedly at 3:00 am with returning to sleep proving to be more elusive than ever? Do you hit the snooze button several times in the morning before dragging yourself wearily out of bed? Are your waking hours plagued with feelings of fatigue, mental fogginess, forgetfulness and low mood?

If you recognise yourself in any of these descriptions, then something is definitely out of kilter with your natural ability to sleep soundly and awake refreshed each morning.

It is impossible to achieve optimum health and wellbeing if your sleep is regularly disrupted. Poor sleep is more than just an inconvenience; after all, enforced sleep deprivation has been used as an effective method of torture over the centuries. The Royal Society for Public Health (RSPH) published a report in April 2016 noting that 10 million prescriptions for sleeping tablets are written by doctors in the UK each year. In their poll of 2000 adults they reported their average sleep time is 6.8 hours compared with the 7.7 hours they felt they needed. This amounts to a sleep deficit of about one hour per night, which cumulatively amounts to losing the equivalent of an entire night's sleep a week.

Poor sleep patterns can have an impact on general health, including an increased risk of many preventable medical conditions, such as obesity, heart disease and diabetes. The immune system is also compromised in its ability to fight infection, while insomnia is a common precursor of an increased risk of anxiety and depression.

How much sleep?

The RSPH report suggested that 18- to 64-year-olds should sleep between seven and nine hours a night. Increased amounts of sleep are recommended for one- to two-year-olds who ideally require 11 to 14 hours per night even though babies and toddlers often seem to be wilfully surviving on the least possible amount of sleep! The sleep requirement for over 65-year-olds falls to seven to eight hours per night.

Sleep hygiene

It is important to consider changing your habits around going to bed and improving your ability to sleep soundly throughout the night. You can use the nudge theory explained on page 11 to nudge yourself towards change and help you to impose new bedtime habits.

For instance, you can use the nudge theory to keep the bedroom an electronics-free zone. If you usually keep your smart phone on your bedside table to use its alarm function, you can nudge a positive change to this habit and purchase a cheap alarm clock as an alternative.

Nudge changes in your behaviour to give yourself a buffer zone between being fully awake and bedtime. Ideally, turn off your computer, TV and phone at least 30 minutes before retiring. This is easy and effortless to achieve if you are nudging changes from watching television to reading a novel in the final hour before bed.

Shower or bathe too if that is something that would help you to unwind.

All of these things are routines that, once established, send messages from your brain that it is time to relax and sleep. They are akin to the sleep training you might have had from your parents as a baby. Somehow, all the good habits you may have learnt have got lost, but you can reclaim them. Psychologists estimate it takes 21 days to embed a new routine until it becomes a habit, so stick with this new behaviour for at least that length of time.

Sleep strategies

To encourage a return to a natural pattern of sleep, it is useful to keep a sleep diary for a week or so to find out exactly what is happening with you. Make a note of when you sleep and wake. You may find from your sleep diary that you are napping during the afternoon or evening. If this is the case, you can experiment with staying awake until mid-night for a couple of weeks without napping so that you are genuinely tired when you finally get to bed.

You may also have developed a habit of believing that going to bed means experiencing long bouts of wakeful tossing and turning. Next time you find yourself in bed and awake, unable to sleep, get up immediately and leave your bedroom. Sit on the sofa without turning on any electronics and stay there until you feel properly tired before returning to bed. It is important to break the conditioning you have developed associating bed with wakefulness and imprint new habits on your mind that bed is for sleeping.

Finally, instead of reading a book at bedtime, remember that sex with yourself or your partner releases waves of the natural feel-good chemical in your brain called dopamine that has a soporific quality, aiding relaxation and sleep.

The breathing habit

Need a new breathing habit? You are probably convinced that you have that one covered as you've been doing it since you were born and it is actually so easy, you even do it in your sleep!

Well, studies have shown that as many as 90 per cent of people – so that is practically all of us – do not breathe correctly to obtain the maximum benefits from this essential process.

Many people's breathing is often very shallow and restrictive, which in turn restricts the life-giving oxygen that every cell in our body needs to survive and flourish. In fact, assessing the capacity of how deeply you are breathing is an accurate measure of how much stress you are experiencing at that time.

The following are the instructions for a simple *Qi Gong* breathing technique. Ideally you would commit five to 10 minutes each morning and grow to enjoy its benefits so much that you are happy to sustain this new habit for the rest of your life.

The rewards are numerous and can improve your general sense of wellbeing, increase clarity of thought, provide more vitality, and even be inspirational.

Qi Gong *instructions*

Start as soon as possible.

It is particularly beneficial to do this exercise outside if you are able to.
- Stand up in a relaxed state with loose shoulders and chest open, knees soft, feet hip distance apart and arms hanging at your sides.
- Take a deep and slow breath in while at the same time very slowly raising your arms from the shoulders to over your head. Keep your neck soft and shoulders down.
- Lower your hands slowly while you breathe slowly out. As you do this, visualise negative energy draining out of your body through your feet into the earth while positive energy enters through the top of your head.
- Repeat slowly for a few moments.

This exercise is very relaxing and hopefully you will sense the tension drain out of your body, leaving you feeling re-energised and re-balanced.

It is only a very basic *Qi Gong* breathing exercise. There are numerous *YouTube* demonstrations where you can follow more complex *Qi Gong* sequences that can be very beneficial, or you may be able to join a local group.

Move that body

The latest figures emerging about the role exercise plays in achieving weight loss show that it accounts for an overall improvement of about 10 per cent and that 90 per cent of weight loss is due to what you eat. However, it does not mean that exercise should be discounted as not being worth the effort. There is a very simple and practical way of helping the brain to increase the levels of feel-good chemicals, such as dopamine and serotonin, and that is moving your body. It works with any activity that provides mild to moderate exertion. Yoga does it. Swimming does it. Cycling does it. And physical activity in its purest and most accessible form – walking – does it too and is natural enough for most people to attempt.

One of the defining characteristics of being alive is movement and a key element in improving your wellbeing is a commitment to walking each and every day.

How much walking?

To get optimum health benefits from walking you need ideally to achieve a minimum of 10,000 steps per day. That's three times more than the average adult manages of approximately 3000 steps per day. The easiest way to keep track of your daily step count is by using a step counter or pedometer.

If including walking in your daily schedule feels like a radical departure for you, it would be advisable to introduce it gradually and build on your daily step count towards the 10,000 steps goal. Begin by logging your step count over a period of a week or so to get an idea of your daily average.

Once you have that, you can begin by adding an additional 500 steps to your daily average, thereafter increasing it every few days until you reach 10,000 steps. Make sure you are wearing good walking shoes or trainers that fully support the arches of your feet and your ankles.

Achieving 10,000 steps per day speeds up your metabolism, helps your gut to clear more regularly, increases circulation and the removal of toxins into the lymphatic system as well as improving your general sense of wellbeing and self-esteem.

Don't be fooled – 10,000 steps is about three miles (or 4.8 km) so at some point you are going to exceed your casual walking commitments and will need to schedule in walks specifically to achieve your step target.

It doesn't need to be walking

For some people, walking 10,000 steps will not be the best or easiest way to schedule in a daily activity. So consider alternatives that appeal to you. Bear in mind when choosing an activity to do regularly that it is best to find something that can give you a real sense of joy – something that you really enjoy doing. For many people, attending a gym can feel like a disheartening and isolating experience, whereas joining a line dancing class, or a Zumba or local salsa dance class, might give you an opportunity to move around more while enjoying being a member of a group who feel they are all in it together.

If you are feeling isolated in your life you can use your goal of moving more to find opportunities to be sociable. Do not perhaps choose a solo activity such as swimming. Gales of laughter from water aerobics groups or water Zumba groups often echo around swimming pools so you can choose to go where the laughter is.

If joining anything at all feels challenging, ask a friend to go with you at least for the first session or two. Alternatively, you can contact the organiser beforehand and tell him or her how nervous you feel as a newbie. How they respond will determine how comfortable and supported you will feel attending their group. You can do a deal with yourself where you agree just to do it once and if you don't like it you never have to go again.

Even walking doesn't have to be solitary activity. Enlist a friend or family member or join a rambling/walking club, a local river clearing squad or a green gym scheme where participants volunteer to work in groups to clear and improve local natural habitat.

Whatever you do, your target is to try and do something every day. An indoor mini-trampoline or rebounder is an ideal way of reaching your 10,000 step target without even leaving your house. You use the same action as walking so it counts the same and is very easy on knee joints. It is also ideal for rainy days.

All activity lifts the mood and changes how you feel so is the perfect complement to everything else you are doing to take the best care of yourself.

Just so you know – a brisk one mile walk accomplished in 20 minutes burns around 100 Kcal. That's as much as swimming for 10 minutes, playing football for 12 minutes or doing aerobics for 16 minutes. Regular walking can also halve your risk of a heart attack, improve circulation, lower blood cholesterol levels, promote an increased sense of wellbeing, improve joint flexibility, build strength in muscles and increase bone density, boost your immune system, help you breathe more efficiently, aid restful sleep and build confidence.

Walking is also reported to have beneficial effects on type 2 diabetes and can be an important factor in managing the condition.

Once you have got into the habit of leaving your office or home at lunch time you will wonder how you ever got through your day without a walking break. Daily regular activity will quickly become a habit that you value and you will be loath to forgo it.

Emotional benefits of walking

Stephania Piazzalunga is a psychotherapist working in Italy and a great advocate for the curative power of walking. She says that it is when we walk that our inner thoughts are revealed to us via a sort of meditation in motion.

She believes that walking in silence or quiet contemplation is one of the most natural and original forms of self-help, with the mere act of moving encouraging an improved sense of wellbeing and self-esteem.

You need never walk alone

Walking is one of the most popular leisure activities in the developed world, with some people dedicating their annual holidays to it. Research shows that there is little left of our planet that has not been trodden on by keen walkers.

If you would like to supplement your regular daily step count with occasional walkabouts into new horizons, but are not sure about going it alone, an easy way to meet fellow walkers is by joining the Ramblers or Walking Association or your local equivalent. Most countries have a network of local groups. You can start with very short walks of 1.5 to 2 miles (2.5 to 3 kilometres) and gradually increase the distance.
You will also benefit from the opportunity of walking with other more

experienced walkers who can provide a wealth of knowledge.

Guided walks are often offered by local groups or municipal organisations which have programmes that often cost very little to join. Check out your local library or local newspapers/websites for more information.

Another good resource is www.meetup.com – this website has some marvelous groups in many cities around the world, with many offering participation free of charge.

Local health providers are also working with volunteers to organise and lead regular Health Walks for people who are working to improve their mobility or recovering from illness. The walks are graded to be suitable for a range of abilities and are a perfect way for you to be supported and encouraged in those early days. Check with your local General Health Practitioner, Health Provider or look online for 'Health Walks' in your area.

Deciding on an actual walking holiday or short break brings up a vast array of possibilities from specialist companies that offer walking activities, while others offer holidays involving different adventures or activities tied into wider interests. Within this specialist field you may find single-sex walking holidays, cultural walks, special interest walks or urban versus country locations. An advantage of this means you will be with like-minded individuals, participating in a shared activity that is a great way for you to meet up with others and enjoy a group experience.

If nothing exists in your neighbourhood, how about starting your own group?

How food influences your mood

Learning to feel differently about food includes recognising the link between nutrition and mental wellbeing. There is no point in achieving a slimmer body if the price is depression and increased anxiety. Scientific researchers suggest people should be cautious in how they reduce their calorie intake while attempting to slim down as research findings show that sudden changes in nutrition, or reducing certain nutrients in a diet, can result in a worsening of depressive symptoms. (Sathyanarayana et al, 2008)

A study in the *British Journal of Psychiatry* (Akbaraly et al, 2009) also found evidence that eating a wide range of real foods versus processed foods of poor nutritional quality increased the likelihood of depression.

When people abruptly stop eating large amounts of processed foods containing unhealthy fats, and loaded with sugar, they can often experience withdrawal symptoms similar to those of going 'cold turkey' from drugs. The withdrawal symptoms can last for several days and for some people the symptoms of headache, muscle pain and feeling below par can be powerful enough for them to return to their old eating habits just to make them feel 'normal' again. Stick with the process, though, as the rewards will far outweigh any temporary discomfort.

Other nutritional deficiencies have a part to play in feeling low or even depressed. These include deficiencies in zinc, omega-3 fats, B vitamins, B6 and B12 especially, and vitamin D.

Missing meals can cause a dip in blood sugar levels, resulting in the release of adrenaline which increases feelings of anxiety and can even be a trigger for raised levels of anxiety generally.

Disordered eating often involves binge eating. This causes physical discomfort but can also often be a trigger for feelings of despair and shame. If overeating happens late at night, the inevitable bloating can interfere with the ability to sleep, again lowering mood.

Following a restrictive diet where carbohydrates are eliminated has an impact on serotonin levels in the brain that can lead to feelings of depression. We encourage eating a balance of complex, unrefined starchy carbohydrates such as vegetables and protein and healthy fats to maintain a positive mood, and promote satiety.

Making changes towards healthier food choices is obviously beneficial on many different levels. The changeover can happen during a radical period when mass changes are made, or one meal at a time, gradually reducing the amount of processed sugars and high fat foods that are eaten. How this is tackled is down to personal choice, and what best suits each individual.

In essence, a healthy diet will not cause ecstatic happiness but a poor diet could be a contributing factor to feeling low, so it's important for mental wellbeing to eat a wide variety of real foods.

Cutting through the confusion

Never before in the history of humankind have we faced a situation where increasing numbers of the older generation are predicted to outlive their offspring. Never before has there been a time with such a wealth of information about what we should and should not eat. Messages bombard us from every angle, in all types of media, from the evermore confusing labelling on food packaging through persuasion from celebrity-endorsed brands to government-funded campaigns, proliferating all over the Western world, and yet we still find ourselves in the middle of an increasing and unprecedented obesity epidemic.

So, with all this information and guidance we should be the healthiest, most nutritionally savvy generation ever to live on Earth – yet this just isn't the case. The 'standard American diet' (SAD) leaves increasing numbers of people overfed yet nutritionally undernourished, contributing to poor general health on a massive scale. The effects were once largely found in industrialised countries, but are now obvious in developing nations too, making this a truly global problem.

It is obvious that the healthy eating message has become so confused and contradictory that even the so-called 'experts' cannot agree on an effective strategy to improve public health. The information overload ultimately amounts to just so much white noise, and in the end we just zone out and ignore it.

The high percentage of people who are currently struggling with their weight, or labelled obese by the medical community, is the greatest challenge of the 21st century. Much of the problem of excessive weight gain and obesity can be laid at the door of the convenience food manufacturers and the proliferation of 24/7 takeaways, with fast-food outlets on every high street. The popularity of sweet drinks; the habit of constantly grazing; snacking while on the move; the lack of structure around meal times – all of this means no-one is sure any more if they are hungry or can recognise when they are full. This is especially true when so much eating happens when busy doing other things. Eating then becomes a secondary activity that is barely registered by the conscious mind.

The majority of today's popular processed foods and soft drinks have been developed in laboratories by men and women in white coats (rather than chef's hats!) with ingredients' lists that read like advanced chemistry. So many multi-syllable, unpronounceable, unrecognisable ingredients go into making Frankenstein-type concoctions of unhealthy fats, sugars and artificial flavourings in a never-ending variety of high profit margin fake foods.
Our taste buds have been assailed for years by an onslaught of synthetic flavours, textures and colours, so that now many people have a hard time knowing what real food should even taste like. These processed foods are so prevalent, and so expertly marketed, it's no wonder we fall victim to them. So-called 'low fat' this, and 'no added sugar' that; we buy them thinking that we are doing ourselves good and eating healthily when in fact we are eating nothing short of a packet full of lies and chemicals. These products are so adulterated they shouldn't even be called 'food'!

The food industry seems to take a perverse delight in conjuring up calorifically loaded foods, sometimes exceeding an adult's entire daily calorie allowance in just a single serving. They love to abracadabra into existence these highly addictive combinations of fats, sugars and artificial flavourings that would never exist in a natural form; to formulate irresistibly tempting 'goop' with huge calorie loads, and absolutely no nutritional value.

Profit-motivated agribusinesses have been allowed unprecedented free rein, in their 'state of the art' laboratories, to genetically modify our crops and adulterate our foods so that many are no longer recognisable from their original, natural state. Much of the research was sanctioned and funded by first world governments with the altruistic aim of ending famine in the third world by developing new strains of crops, more resistant to blight, and to increase yields in poor growing conditions. All of this was done with the best of intentions. However, the ramifications of the unfettered, profit-hungry agribusinesses are only now becoming known and many of these outcomes are not so beneficial. The true effect of these practices is often obscured by profit margins and vested interests.

For instance, these very same agribusinesses have turned natural seasonal eating into whole-year-round availability of every type of fruit and vegetable, flown in from every corner of the globe. Sounds fine in theory perhaps, except the essential micro-nutrients in these once seasonal foods are now hugely reduced due to their being grown with the use of excessive pesticides, or force-grown under plastic, or picked before ripened, so that they can be flown to distribution hubs thousands of miles away.

The food giants manufacture a vast range of cans of carbonated soft drinks, energy drinks and sodas containing excessive sugar, artificial sweeteners, caffeine, phosphorus and carbon acids, all of which can cause harmful effects to the body.

Collectively, the efforts of the food manufacturing giants have normalised a way of eating that would seem alien to our grandmothers' generation. We often play with the idea of the mythical 'grandmother' test to judge if a food or a food process would comply with real food guidelines. The restaurant critic and food writer Jay Rayner (2015) wrote in *The Observer Food Magazine*, 'Whenever I hear a pursed-lipped food campaigner announce that we should only eat things our grandmothers would recognise, my first thought is that my grandmother was a lousy cook, and I'd fight to keep her away from the kitchen.'

For our purposes, our grandmothers would really have known their stuff and would have been great scratch cooks, working with real ingredients to create wholesome meals. They would certainly have had no time for the many radical changes in food production and eating habits that have led to a year upon year increase in worldwide obesity rates since the end of the Second World War (Academic Earth, 2015).

While these changes have been taking place, many consumer-focused organisations and spokespeople who are in positions of power and influence, and who should have been on the lookout for the ordinary consumer, have been silent. Instead, they made themselves profitable alliances with the food giants. These alliances have contributed to creating a complex web of conflicts of interest, on an international scale.

It would be absurd and laughable if it wasn't true. Take for instance the Academy of Nutrition and Dietetics. With over 75,000 members, it is the largest association of food and nutritional professionals in the world. In very recent times their membership has applied pressure for the organisation to relinquish some of its questionable connections to food manufacturing giants that have included Coca-Cola, Kraft Foods, Nestlé, Hershey's, PepsiCo and McDonald's. Their current sponsors are listed on their Meet Our Sponsors page and still include PepsiCo (Eat right pro, 2016). They have given approval and allowed these monolithic conglomerates, and many others besides, to provide educational material for their own organisation that, by association, blurs health issues and confuses the public.

When London hosted the Olympic Games in 2012, the International Olympic Committee squandered the opportunity of promoting a positive healthy-eating message by agreeing to sponsorship from fast-food manufacturers McDonald's along with Coca-Cola and Cadbury's chocolate.

McDonald's opened its largest restaurant in the world right inside the Olympic Park, and Coca-Cola expected to serve over 20,000,000 fizzy drinks at the Games, benefiting as it did from its near monopoly at Olympic venues. It is the potential conflicts of interest such as these that obscure clear messages around nutrition and are one of the reasons why people feel so overwhelmed, and confused about what to eat.

Our aim in this book is to show you how you can cut through all the hype, debunk all the myths and confusion, and eat for nutrition, weight loss if appropriate, and optimum mental and physical health.

Kurtay's kitchen story

My interest in feeling differently about food and improving my eating habits was motivated by my desire to cure myself of multiple sclerosis (MS). I was diagnosed when I was 19 years old and not surprisingly it felt like a devastating blow. I felt overwhelmed and pretty powerless for a long time. Going into therapy and undertaking my own research made me want to be proactive about my own health. My thinking shifted to such an extent that I felt empowered to improve my health. Everything I've read and studied over the years always comes back to the importance of nutrition.

I find that eating salads, mainly green leaves, along with grilled fish, such as salmon, sea-bass and fresh tuna, makes me feel more energised. I also find starting the day with a home-made green juice helps me to feel mentally sharper and physically more ready for the day ahead. My favourite recipe is a handful of kale, fresh spinach, stick of celery, a carrot, a small piece of fresh turmeric, a crisp, green apple with fresh lemon or lime all juiced together. I add coconut water until it has the right consistency to drink. It's delicious.

I have lived with the diagnosis of MS for over 10 years now and my body soon tells me when I am working to help it or hinder it. If I've had a few days of not eating well, or eating on the run as I've been too busy to prepare the food I know works for me, the contrast in how I feel and how much energy I have is astounding. What I choose to eat has a very tangible effect on my health, and eating real food makes me feel I can play a positive role in managing my condition and one day over-turning this diagnosis.

The one piece of advice I have for anyone considering switching from processed foods to real foods is that only you can help yourself, so stop asking and start acting – your body will thank you for it.

You can follow Kurtay on Twitter: @Kurtaytoros83

Just eat real food

Human beings, supposedly at the top of the food chain, are the only creatures on Earth who are confused about what to eat. Wild animals do not turn to experts, or stress themselves out about what they should or should not eat – they are just focused on getting enough. Nor do they obsess by weighing or measuring everything. They simply eat when they are hungry, stop when they are full, and consume what is available in their environment, appropriate for their bodies.

If further proof is required as to the level of confusion there is around what food choices to make, then ponder this: Eating real food is in itself a movement. It goes by many names too. One of the emergent names for this kind of eating is 'paleo' which is shorthand for Paleolithic. This was an era in history dating back some 2.6 million years. There are many definitions of what paleo means. Some people can get very animated about what qualifies as 'real' paleo, and what does not. The term has been around for less than a decade yet it has already spawned specific approaches and conflicting opinions, the names of some of which are listed here.

Ancestral diet	Farmist or farmarians
Bare food eating	JERF – Just Eat Real Food
Cave girl/man diet	Neanderthal diet
Cross fit diet	Primal raw diet
Evolutionary diet	Slow food revolution
Evolved diet	Traditional diet

It is practically impossible to know accurately what our ancestors ate all those millennia ago – and this would of course have varied hugely with latitude, climate and terrain – and yet the desire to return to simple, unprocessed foods is gaining in popularity as people search for a way to combat the increasing incidence of modern diseases, such as diabetes, obesity, cancer, autoimmune diseases and heart disease.

Our take on traditional eating in essence means focusing on unprocessed, real foods that incorporate sources of protein and healthy fats together with a wide selection of vegetables, some dairy (unless not tolerated), and smaller amounts of nuts, fruit and seeds. Most importantly of all is for each individual to find his or her own healthy, enjoyable and sustainable way of eating. This is not a fad diet. In fact, it's not a 'diet' at all. Neither is it about expensive pills, or supplements, meal replacements, cereal bars or any other kind of fake food.

Working with our clients we focus on eating real foods that are nutritionally rich and promote a healthy body and mind. We give you a framework and encourage you to adapt it to fit your own needs and lifestyle.

Food researcher and author Michael Pollen said everything he's learned about food and health can be summed up in seven words: 'Eat food, not too much, mostly plants.'

The key word here is food. Real food. We show you what to buy and how to eat the very best food you can source – good quality, organic if you can, non-GM, free-range, pesticide free, locally grown, seasonal, fresh or frozen. This is about taking the very best care of yourself with the very best food you can source according to your budget.

Sharon's kitchen story

I often felt tired and lethargic and had lots of uncomfortable digestive issues, including terrible heartburn. It had reached the point that it was affecting my ability to function on a day-to-day basis, and I was finding it more difficult to focus at work too. My brain felt constantly foggy and I was having really bad mood swings. I also had an itch which felt like my skin was crawling on the inside; it used to dive me crazy.

My partner got frustrated with me feeling grim and she did endless internet research and suggested that we should focus on our nutrition. I wasn't convinced and for my birthday she took me to a paleo/real food restaurant that had recently opened. I loved the food and their philosophy so much that after that I went home and started to do my own research. I was hooked! A whole new way of thinking was opening up for me about using food as medicine to heal the body. It can feel like quite a lot to get your head around at first so it was just small steps at a time. The hardest thing to do was to give up sugar. It felt harder than when I quit smoking years ago.

Since switching my diet to real food my head has felt clearer and my digestive issues have all but disappeared. I feel clean on the inside just from eating real food. I have so much more energy and want to get out of bed in the mornings and I can easily concentrate at work for eight hours.

My lunchbox is usually leftovers from the previous night's dinner which we cook from scratch. I also put aside half a day on the weekend and prepare a couple of slow-cooked casseroles to freeze in serving-size containers which are then available for lunches or dinners. They are really handy if you're a bit pressed for time during the week.

A dinner favourite is a good old chicken curry cooked in an electric pressure cooker. For people pressed for time, an electric pressure cooker is perfect. You can have meat falling off the bone in 25 minutes. Just put all the ingredients in and put the lid on. Turn it on and forget about it. I go and have a shower and half an hour later have a delicious meal ready to go.

Since I've been eating real food I've noticed how good I feel and how much better I sleep at night. I feel happy on the inside and with a healthy body comes a healthy mind. My eyes and skin are clear and my hair is really shiny and lustrous. I used to get really bloated and that has gone too. Heartburn is no more and that weird inner itch has completely disappeared. I just feel really good!

My words of advice for someone considering changing how they think and feel about food is to not give up. It's a big change in lifestyle, that's what it is. Eating real food and cooking fresh, nutritional meals is not a fad diet. It's a lifestyle choice. You will most likely go through a period of your body detoxing from chemicals and processed food and you may feel initially more tired and possibly get headaches too. However, you will come out the other side and start bouncing around feeling marvellous. People will ask you what are you doing because you will naturally lose weight and look healthier.

My final advice is to go through your kitchen cupboards and put all processed foods in a box and give it to charity. Just ditch it. That way you won't be tempted back into your old ways.

How to make practical changes

Our philosophy is to provide you with a guiding hand to help you make simple and wonderful changes to what you eat, so that you can eat for optimum nutrition and feel marvellous, all at the same time. However, there are no absolutes here. If you choose to make only small changes to your food choices you will still be making some beneficial improvements. Do not berate yourself if you return to your old, less healthy eating habits occasionally, or if you do not feel able to fully embrace a radical change to all of your meals all at once.

For many people, small, incremental steps have proven to be the most successful way for them to make radical and long-lasting changes in their lives. Therefore, although we wholeheartedly would love you to fully embrace and follow all our guidelines, we recognise that ultimately this is your call.

This is not an opportunity to feel bad about yourself; that is the complete opposite of what this book is about. So, take your time and implement changes in how you shop, cook and eat at your own pace. And, if you decide you can only face changing one meal out of your day for now, then that's fine too. Many of the people we have worked with have adopted this method, and by making changes initially to their breakfasts, for instance, they have been able to gradually prepare and cook different foods for themselves and even for their families. Instead of setting yourself up to fail, introduce and manage these changes in the way that is best suited for you to guarantee your success.

We show you how to eat real, natural foods, all of which are readily available in your usual supermarket but just in different aisles. We show you how to cook with convenient short cuts, because we know how busy our clients and readers are, living and working full lives with little time to spare.

After just a few days of cutting out fake foods and eating real food you will reap the benefits of improved mood stability, increased energy, improved mental focus, better sleep patterns, shinier hair, clearer skin and stronger nails, as well as feelings of greater wellbeing. You'll be hooked. And, you'll do all of this by never going hungry, and without any sense of deprivation. That's a promise.

You will never again want to return to eating foods that only provide you with meagre nutrition, that bloat and exhaust you. You will realise that starchy, simple carbohydrate foods, or foods high in sugar and saturated fats, are a way of eating for punishment and to hurt yourself, and they simply will not appeal to you any more. You will find yourself becoming increasingly aligned and focused on only wanting to eat good-quality, nutritious foods.

Many of our clients report that once they start eating the appetising foods we recommend their whole family wants to eat the same meals too. The bonus of your own healthy eating contributes to increased wellbeing for your partner and children or other relatives or friends, without them even realising they are making radical changes to the way they eat.

We cut out all the confusion from what you should and shouldn't eat by simply taking you back to the basics, by following some logical, commonsense guidance, and presenting it in a straightforward and easy-to-follow way.

When you learn about which foods are good for you and how much you need to eat in a day, as well as which foods you would be advised to avoid or minimise, it puts you in control of your health and your life. Making the right choices for yourself according to your needs, appropriate to what is happening in your life, is key to obtaining that all-important balance between achieving healthy weight-loss and maximising wellbeing.

By following the food principles explained here you can be sure to see real results. The difference this time is that we are trading in intensive food restriction for authentic change over a much longer period with greater enduring benefits.

Ceri's kitchen story

It was recommended I switch to a real-food/paleo way of eating by my fitness teacher, who was also a trained nutritionist. It made sense to me as a way of streamlining my eating in a positive way to help fuel the long runs I was doing as part of my training to run a marathon. I was wary of the damage marathon running could do to my body and wanted to make sure I was in tiptop health. I'd only ever eaten masses of pasta and porridge to fuel long-distance running in the past and found I was always insatiably hungry so I thought there had to be a better solution. I was looking for weight loss too, hoping that as a slim-line gazelle version of my former self I might run faster. Within two weeks of eating differently I was blown away by how good I felt and how much weight and fat percentage I had lost.

That was a few years ago now and I went on to train as a chef, eventually qualifying at Bauman College in Berkeley, California as a Natural Chef in 2014. These days I work as a recipe developer and cooking instructor and it's safe to say my store cupboards are bursting at the seams with a wide array of ingredients, some of which go up and down in my favour. However, I always have to hand in my kitchen free-range eggs, fresh lemons, extra virgin olive oil if nothing else. Cumin is my favourite spice and gives great flavour to anything it is added to. I also try to incorporate fermented foods into my diet and make up a batch of sauerkraut when I can, but I can't profess to always being that organised. I just don't beat myself up about it!

A julienne peeler or a spiraliser are a popular addition to many kitchens these days to create courgette spaghetti (courgetti) and it is a great way to get over a pasta addiction. I add warm courgetti alongside meat dishes and salmon fillets or have them on their own with my old repertoire of classic Italian sauces such as carbonara. They are also great cold tossed in pesto for a salad. When a change of flavour-base from Italian is in order they can be thrown into Asian-inspired dishes such as Pad Thai.

If I'm going somewhere where I have no idea if there will be any nutritious foods on offer, then I always take a tin of fish. The fish can be eaten on their own in desperate times, but more often than not they can be added to a side salad for a proper balanced meal. I'm not a fan of snacking on nuts because it's easy to overeat on them and they don't suit my digestion, so mostly I prefer to snack on vegetable crudités, or fruit.

Plantains are having a bit of a moment in my kitchen. I know they are very starchy, even more than a potato, but they make great pancakes, tortillas, wraps or chips or can just simply be roasted and tossed into a salad. My theory is that if you can replace a white grain or a generally unhealthily prepared food with a vegetable, then it has to be all good.

I love to make my own pesto or any kind of herb/garlic/olive oil/ lemon juice/salt/spices-style dressing, so I usually blend one of these up to drizzle over a meal. A current favourite of mine is using anchovies in a sauce – like a salsa verde. They give such depth of flavour and an omega 3 boost at the same time as they are a nutritionally rich oily fish.

I often get told that I have great skin, bright eyes and shiny hair. I suffered from acne a lot in my late teens and early 20s so it's a delight to know my diet has helped turn this around. If I make sure that I'm looking after my stress levels and getting enough sleep and gentle exercise, then this in combination with my eating real food helps balance my energy levels and boost my immunity so I get ill very infrequently. If you're eating well but not sleeping properly, then you can't guarantee you will always be on top form. I know from personal experience!

It can take a while to find your own way to feel differently about food. I now mix paleo elements with a real-food philosophy, with the usual amount of treats and odd deviations. It has taken me a long time to get here. I used to worry about what pure paleo'ists would think and for a while I was afraid to admit that I had introduced dairy, legumes and some grains like buckwheat and oats back into my life. I've personally found that sticking rigidly to rules can lead to obsessive behaviour which is not healthy for anyone.

You can find out more about Ceri's work as a natural chef, food writer and healthy cookery teacher at www.naturalkitchenadventures.com

Master your breakfasts

If you are a person who skips breakfast, especially if you are hungry, or eats one of the popular toast-cereal, or muesli-and-juice-type combinations, then you are going to feel radically better eating any of the suggestions that follow.

Our breakfast alternatives avoid causing a blood sugar spike when you eat. When sugar is released into the bloodstream from standard carbohydrate-laden breakfast fayre this sets you up for a sugar slump later in the day, leaving you feeling exhausted and foggy-brained. In comparison, you'll be amazed how full and satisfied you will feel eating foods that include protein and healthy fats.

This is going to require some forward planning on your part by way of shopping, and perhaps some bulk weekend cooking. These investments in your time and energy will give you healthy eating options for the whole week, and will be especially appreciated later when time is really pressured.

We are about to debunk a popular myth. We have been told for decades that breakfast is the most important meal of the day. Who told us? We might have assumed it was nutritional experts, or medical professionals, but it turns out it was the breakfast cereal manufacturers in the 1950s who funded massive advertising campaigns that promoted this particular fiction so effectively.

We have also been told the myth that obese people are often the ones who skip breakfast. The theory then goes that without breakfast they are driven to constant food grazing or overeating during the rest of the day, leading to weight gain.

According to the research published in the March 2016 edition of the *American Journal of Clinical Nutrition* (Chowdhury et al, 2016) there is scant scientific evidence to support the theory that breakfasts are a vital component of our daily food intake. Dr James Betts, the lead researcher, found that neither obese people who ate breakfast nor those who skipped it lost weight. Betts also found that people who did not eat breakfast did not consume additional calories later in the day but instead conserved their energy by being less active. This behaviour difference can cumulatively over several days equal burning fewer calories than those who ate breakfast.

If anything, the typical Western, or 'standard American diet' (SAD) with a breakfast made up of grain-based cereals, or muesli with milk, or toasted bread topped with sugar-laden jams or marmalade, is nothing more than a health hazard, and a possible trigger for many allergies as well. So, if you are hungry in the morning and want to eat breakfast, then we think you should maximise the nutritional value of this meal, just as we would recommend you would for all your meals. Equally, if you are not hungry, then do not feel you have to eat breakfast. Key to feeling differently about food is that you only need to eat when you are hungry. It is as simple as that.

Breakfast is often the most time-pressured meal of the day. This first meal is often skipped, even if you are hungry, as there never seems to be enough time to eat anything before dashing out of the door to make the school run or to join the commuter throng.

Interestingly, in our therapy work with clients who come to see us with anxiety issues, or panic attacks, a common trait is that they regularly skip breakfast. If you eat dinner at around 7 to 8 pm, then do not eat again until lunchtime the next day, you are in effect fasting for over 16 hours. It is similar to the pattern of eating that has become well known as 'intermittent fasting' (IF), the most popular version of which recommends two days of fasting (500 cals per day) interspersed with five days of normal or slightly reduced portion sizes for the rest of the week. It primarily does not dictate what foods you should or should not eat but rather focuses on when you should eat instead. It can work very well for some people who say they prefer the time constraints as opposed to having to consider what they actually eat.

The health benefits of IF require further scientific investigation but are thought to lead to improvements in general health and may have potential benefits for anti-ageing, preventing cancer and boosting cognitive function as well as having other medical benefits including quite often weight loss

(Hall 2015 quoting Mattson et al, 2014 and Varady and Hellerstein 2007).

However, not everyone is emotionally or even physically suited to intermittent fasting and some people do not easily tolerate the extended periods of hunger. For instance, if you are already experiencing anxiety and stress, the inevitable low blood sugar levels and an empty, growling belly on a fasting day can set the stage for some people to experience heightened emotional responses. In addition, it is acknowledged that a wide variation in blood sugar levels, caused by skipping meals, can lead to hormonal disturbances, and common symptoms of this are fatigue and feeling below par. If you decide to try IF for yourself you could consider setting yourself shorter periods of fasting to begin with and increase the fasting periods as you build up your confidence that this pattern of eating works for you without any adverse effects.

The decision whether to eat breakfast or not can be confidently made depending on if you are hungry and if you have an appetite for it. If you do not, then you can skip it. If you experience heightened anxiety, or panic attacks (which can be caused by hypoglycemia – low blood sugar), it is worth experimenting with how you feel after eating breakfast along the lines we recommend for a while and noting any improvements in your emotional balance and moods by, as recommended before, keeping a food mood diary (see page 127). If you do notice a reduction in your anxiety levels, then adopting a nutritionally rich breakfast could easily become part of your own self-care regime.

For some people, the idea of eating anything shortly after waking is nausea-inducing. They are the very people who might grab a tall caramel latte on their way to work. We provide nutritious alternatives below for those who eat their first meal of the day away from home too. We show you how, with a little planning, you can eat something nourishing and sustaining without compromising your morning's tight schedule. This way, you will be gifting your body with the protein and healthy fats (see page 78) you need to feel ready for the challenges of your day, feeling more alert and with increased mental focus.

Start your day with an egg

During the 1950s, an advertising campaign advised 'Go to work on an egg' to encourage UK families to eat more eggs. Now that once-popular slogan feels like nothing more than an antiquated piece of postwar propaganda. In recent decades people have become much more wary of eating eggs. The decline in the popularity of this cheap and nutritious food is linked with several high-profile salmonella scares and – more effectively – the frequently reported heath warnings linking raised cholesterol levels to egg consumption.

More recently it has been acknowledged by experts the world over that it is not necessary on health grounds to exclude or limit your intake of eggs. The new wisdom is that eggs are again acknowledged as one of the most nutritious foods money can buy, and a rich source of many nutrients, including high quality protein, vitamins and minerals.

Overall, it has been decreed that eating eggs is perfectly safe. Studies have ascertained that for ordinary, healthy people who do not have any pre-existing health concerns, it is perfectly safe to eat up to three eggs per day, most days. Studies haven't exceeded that daily quantity so the jury is out on whether more eggs per day would eventually prove to be detrimental or more than just a little dull.

All eggs are not equal. Your average supermarket eggs are from chickens that are raised in restricted living conditions and unnaturally fed grain-based feed. Choose organic eggs from hens that are allowed to roam free. Free-range eggs will taste better and are naturally much higher in omega-3 oils, and important fat-soluble vitamins, plus you will be supporting humane treatment of these intelligent birds.

A healthy portion of protein means a serving of a minimum two eggs. They can be hard-boiled, scrambled, poached or fried. You can serve them with a couple of good quality bacon rashers or a high-standard butcher's sausage if you like. You can add in tomatoes and mushrooms too.

A two- or three-egg omelette takes literally two minutes to cook and the eggs can be premixed in advance, and left in a bowl in the fridge overnight. Stir in any leftover vegetables too. You can save time by cooking your sausage and bacon the night before while preparing your dinner.

Exceptions to the health benefits of eggs are caused by a chemical contained in egg whites called lysozyme, plus high levels of histamine in the whites. Most people, even those who have an egg allergy, will find they are fine with the yolks. Lysozyme is found in large quantities in egg white and can in rare circumstances form globules of molecules in the gut and add to existing gut problems. Eggs are such a wonderful source of protein and healthy omega oils that we recommend you only exclude them from your diet if you have been diagnosed with an autoimmune disease, or an allergy, or have found by doing an elimination diet that they really do not agree with you.

In some parts of Continental Europe, breakfasts are a veritable feast of cold cuts of meat, including sliced ham and roast pork served with hard-boiled eggs and a variety of cheeses. Go European and follow their lead. If you are including cheese then select soft or hard goats' cheeses as they are less allergenic than cheese made from cows' milk.

Quiches made with a protein-rich almond based crust (page 58) instead of the traditional carbohydrate-laden pastry can be made at the weekend and provide you with enough helpings to get you through a week of tasty breakfasts.

Frittata can also be made at the weekend to provide a whole week's worth of servings. Made with organic, free-range eggs and a rainbow mix of onions and vegetables, it will provide many wholesome breakfasts with absolutely no additional effort. Frittata is simply a crust-free quiche. It is very adaptable and can be made with either leftover vegetables or mixed frozen veg, and is delicious served hot or cold. Simply gently fry chopped onions in olive oil or ghee, with a clove or two of peeled and crushed garlic until softened. Add the other chopped vegetables (your choice) and continue to fry until the edges of the vegetables become brown and caramelised. This makes them tastier. Season with black pepper and sea salt before pouring in a quantity of pre-whisked eggs. If you are preparing enough for the week you may need to use a dozen eggs, or if you're making enough for a supper just for yourself then two or three eggs would suffice. Cook it gently until the bottom of the frittata sets and then finish it off under a grill to cook the rest of the egg mixture. You can ring the changes by adding in grated cheese, pre-cooked bits of bacon or ham too. Slices of frittata or quiche both travel quite well so are ideal for lunches away from home. Also, instead of using a frying pan or quiche dish to cook a whole dish, use deep muffin tins to bake individual servings in the oven.

Nuts, seeds and omega oils

Porridge has a place in our psyche as something warming and comforting to eat. Paleo-approved porridge retains all of those feel-good factors but replaces possible genetically modified grains with healthier alternatives. They include coconut flour, ground linseeds or ground nuts mixed into a soft paste with coconut milk, or coconut water. You can even make a porridge with the flesh of pre-roasted, or tinned, butternut squash. Add a teaspoon of cinnamon and a drop of vanilla essence, and it just takes a moment in a non-stick pan to heat through. You can add a few fresh or frozen berries to the dish as well.

It is important to remember when planning to include nuts and seeds in your meals that they need to be pre-soaked, preferably overnight, to make them more digestible. Eat a variety of nuts to ensure you achieve a healthy mix of polyunsaturated fatty acids. Omega-3 and omega-6 are the two main types of fatty acids to keep an eye on and ensure you get enough of in your diet for your body to function well. It is probable that our ancestors ate a diet with an omega-6 to omega-3 ratio of about 1:1. Our modern eating habits have drifted far from this ration so that the SAD (Standard American diet) indicates an omega-6 to omega-3 ratio ranging between 15:1 to 17:1. Although you need both omega-6 and omega-3, achieving the right ratio is important as too much omega-6 and too little omega-3 are among the causes for many diseases in the modern world. These two fatty acids have opposite effects when it comes to cardiovascular health and possible inflammatory response in the body (GB HealthWatch 2016).

Walnuts and Brazil nuts are a good source of omega-6 fatty acids and hazelnuts, almonds and especially macadamia nuts, are a good source of omega-3 fatty acids. Dietary guidelines recommend a ratio of omega-6 to omega-3 of 4:1; however, in Japan, where lifespan is longest , they eat a ratio of 2:1 or even 1:1.

Juices and smoothies

A juicer or smoothie maker opens up your breakfast horizon to a world of freshly juiced, raw fruit and vegetable drinks, ideal for a breakfast packed chock full of nutrients and enzymes. Major on dark green vegetables, juiced with minimal amounts of fruit. A cored apple, or a few berries along with a piece of fresh ginger, is all that is needed to balance the taste of kale and spinach. These drinks can be absolutely delicious even if it takes you a while to get used to their vibrant taste. Smoothies have the added benefit of retaining all the fibre, which helps slow down the release of fructose (a type of sugar found in fruit) into the bloodstream. Calcium is also more bio-available to the body from raw, green leafy vegetables than from dairy, so yet another reason to increase your intake of greens.

Kirsty's kitchen story

My interest in eating real food began a few years back now. I had been overtraining with tough, physically challenging sessions two or three times a week for about a year and yet I still hadn't achieved the body I wanted. I had thought I was pretty fit and had set myself the challenge of taking part in a duathlon only to drop out at the 20 km (12 miles) mark feeling completely exhausted.

I knew I was doing everything I could do physically but something needed to change and I realised the missing piece of the jigsaw was my eating habits. I had always existed on a diet of crumpets, bread, cake, pancakes and chocolate, thinking that I could eat whatever I wanted and negate the effects with exercise. I learnt the hard way that you can't.

I began working out with a new trainer who was also nutritionally qualified. She recommended that I cut out grains, sugar, dairy and alcohol for one month and just see how I felt. It's now several years later and I still abide by those rules and benefit from being slimmer and fitter and feeling healthier than ever before, with loads more stamina and energy.

When I decided to feel differently about food I found the key is preparation. On days when I haven't prepared my meals in advance by filling the fridge with pre-prepared veg, boiled eggs, cooked meats/fish or a batch of cooked sweet potato, then making nutritious food choices becomes much more difficult and the temptation to stray is harder to resist.

One thing I've learnt is that I don't need to prepare different foods as meals and snacks. My snacks are often 'mini meals', such as leftovers from the night before. One of my favourites is homemade meatballs. I make them in batches and freeze them. My recipe includes loads of extra veggies chopped into them so they are really tasty and nutritious.

I'll also prep a lunch box the night before so I can take it to work with me the next day. It might be some salmon, baked egg muffins with spinach or perhaps turkey or chicken with two or three different vegetables and maybe some chunks of sweet potato if I'm training that day. I'll probably have a few nuts with me too in a little box. It's so easy to overeat on these so I never take a whole packet out with me. I might well have some berries with me too if they're in season, or a couple of squares of dark chocolate.

Hard-boiled eggs are always a good standby for when I'm dashing out of the house. If I'm out and haven't prepared anything I can often buy beef jerky. (It can come in quite handy, although you have to check the label as some brands can be loaded with junk.) I also like to have something green with everything I eat, even if it's just a handful of spinach leaves straight from the bag.

I'm a chocoholic and would find it very difficult to stick to any eating programme that excluded chocolate. Luckily I've learnt to love the dark 85% cocoa sort but anything above 70% cocoa is classed as healthy when eaten in moderation. Spices and herbs are also vital to keep your food varied and tasty. Lots of people think that eating real food is boring, and it would be without seasoning. No-one wants to be eating plain grilled chicken breast with broccoli every day – it is your chance to get creative.

Currently my favourite meal for dinner is salmon pan-fried in coconut oil with courgette spaghetti, or stir-fried vegetables and various spices with an egg cracked over the top and stirred in. Throw some coconut aminos over it for an awesome soy sauce substitute! Spaghetti made from vegetables like courgettes or sweet potato is great. It is so easy to make your own with a julienne peeler and takes two minutes to cook in a wok. So much quicker than pasta and a lot more nutritious too!

Since I started eating this way I have found that I have more energy and more focus. I sleep better, my mood is stable and I wake up at the same time consistently every morning. What I really love about how I eat is that at the core it's just about eating foods that are what they are. Keep a food/mood diary and understand what triggers your old eating habits to creep back in; don't beat yourself up, but learn from your mistakes and move on. Feeling differently about food began as something I did just for me but it has grown to be my passion and I've gone on to study nutrition and fitness. Based in London I specialise in nutrition and fitness for pre- and postnatal mums. I love supporting women to regain their lost energy levels, teach them how to make sound nutritional choices and create good real food habits to last a lifetime.

The fast food culture we live in isn't set up for eating real food and you'll have to work at it at first until the habits become ingrained, but it's so worth it. Good luck!

You can find out more about Kirsty's work at
http://yummymummynutrition.co.uk/

Healthy-eating ratios

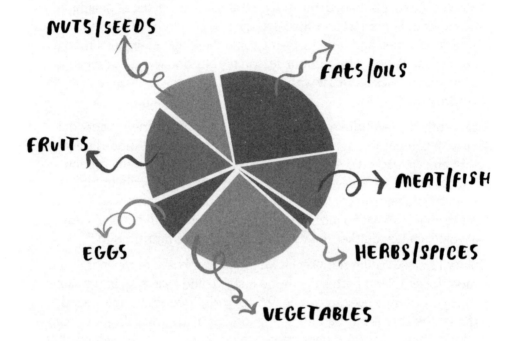

Figure 1 (above) gives you a visual representation of a healthy eating ratio as a guide to what relative amounts to eat. There are no absolute rules here as there is no one-size-fits-all. As our readers, you are all individuals, considering making healthy changes, at different stages of your lives. We recommend the simplest way for you to find a new balanced way to eat is to eat what feels natural for you within our guidelines. Roughly what seems to be healthiest is 10-30 per cent protein, 15 per cent fat and the remainder from vegetables with a 10 to 15 per cent serving of fruit. You will need to find the ratio that works best for your body and life-style. We recommend you keep track with our food/mood diary (see page 127) to see how much animal protein you eat, along with the other food ratios, and how it all makes you feel. You can adjust the amounts of healthy fats and protein to see how this affects your digestion and energy levels to find the optimum ratios for you.

Ideally, during the day, aim to eat some healthy fat; some animal, fish or egg protein; an ample serving of colourful vegetables; small optional portions of different types of fruits, in particular berries; and maybe some nuts. We have discovered that an enhanced feeling of wellbeing is most successfully achieved when adopting a higher-fat, moderate-level-of-protein regime with ample servings of salad, or vegetables. In essence, this is low carbohydrate eating. The carbohydrates we recommend you do eat tend to be from root vegetables instead of grains. We particularly recommend swapping the humble potato for nutrient-dense alternatives such as carrot, beetroot, sweet potato, parsnip, turnip, Jerusalem artichoke and celeriac. Remember, many of these root vegetables work exceedingly well when grated into salads to make a more substantial meal, and when eaten raw less of the starches in the roots are converted into sugar in the body.

Figure 1 (opposite) also indicates a higher proportion than you may have expected of good, healthy fats. We explain which ones to choose in more detail later (see page 78). It may feel counter-intuitive after decades of being encouraged to eat a low-fat diet and challenging at the very least to eat extra fats and oils. However, if you throw away all the low-fat spreads and low-fat yoghurts you usually buy, and replace them with olive oil and full-fat yoghurt, then that will be a move in the right direction. Also, include oil-rich fish a couple of times a week, such as salmon or mackerel, as these are high in omega-3 essential fatty acids that are fundamental to good mental health. Eating avocados and salads with virgin-olive-oil-based dressings will also add up to increasing your daily intake of healthy fat.

To download the A4 printer-friendly PDF version of the food and mood diary template go to www.feeldifferently.co.uk and click on Therapy Tools see Worksheets tab.

Michelle's kitchen story

My initial interest in feeling differently about food came about by accident when I received a flyer in the mail box about a new restaurant opening nearby based on paleo or 'caveman' principles of eating.

The restaurant also happened to be endorsed by the Coeliac Association which grabbed my attention as my partner had problems with food allergies and digestive issues.

I could not wait for us to try the place. Eating there turned out to be a complete eye opener for us. With S's allergies we had practically given up restaurants so it felt really special for us even to be able to eat out let alone enjoy a whole three-course meal.

That is when our journey really began. Buoyed up from our experience of eating nutritious meals without any processed ingredients we continued researching online finding blogs and recipes and learning how to feel differently about food. We are now on a mission learning about new ways of cooking and eating and we follow research online into the mind-body connection which acknowledges the link between food and physical and mental wellbeing.

The changes in S's digestive health from just eating real food have been amazing. No more discomfort or bloating. She's like a new woman. As for me, I found after taking a break from training and the sport I had previously enjoyed all my life I had put on a few extra kilos. Within a couple of weeks of eating in this new way I had shed the excess weight and now easily maintain a healthy, stable weight ... amazing!

Our kitchen cupboards have been transformed and would not be complete without coconut and almond flour to bake, dust, crumb or thicken a variety of foods; and coconut oil and free range eggs to make pancakes for either savoury or sweet fillings. It's also great and cost effective to buy in bulk raw organic ingredients such as grass-fed meat. There are some great online suppliers these days.

At the moment one of my favourite meals is bacon and egg pancakes or a double BLT with hard-boiled eggs mixed with home-made mayonnaise served in a pancake-style burger bun. For tonight's dinner I'm making a chicken meatloaf with fresh, home-grown herbs. Sometimes I substitute chicken with turkey or pork mince to add variety and I'll serve it with sweet potato and pumpkin mash and some fresh greens. For the weekend I'm planning to attempt a yeast-free buckwheat pizza base using home-made tomato sauce and making the topping of whatever is in the fridge.

Since I've changed to eating real food I've noticed my mood over the time has been on a much more even keel. I'm also able to concentrate for longer periods of time and have lots more energy. My complexion is a lot brighter and my skin is generally clear and feels softer. I could not believe my initial weight loss was so quick; I have now stabilised at a weight I am more than happy with.

My advice if you wish to explore feeling differently about food is to start eliminating and substituting foods, perhaps one meal at a time. Choose a meal like lunch for instance and begin to make changes to that meal before attempting to alter your whole diet. Also it is hard to suddenly cut out sugar and high carbs if you have been used to eating them for all your life, so maybe do that gradually or you could be setting yourself up to fail.

Finally, don't be too hard on yourself. It's not the end of the world if you cheat occasionally. It's all about getting back to basics really with eating unprocessed and pure ingredients, and being more organised and motivated for your own benefit and for your whole family's wellbeing.

Eat the rainbow

We advocate eating real food that includes large servings of plant matter. This means vegetables, fruit and selected nuts. These are foods that are rarely sold with a label stuck on them! They are all full of essential vitamins and minerals, especially when eaten raw in salads. The wider the variety of foods you eat, the more variety of vital micro-nutrients you will consume that will support your mood and way of thinking as well as your general health

Antioxidants are natural compounds that help neutralise free radicals in our bodies. Free radicals are substances that occur naturally in our bodies but attack the fats, protein and the DNA in our cells and can cause different types of diseases as well as accelerating the ageing process. Carrots, pumpkins, squash, sweet potato, beetroots, peppers and blueberries are full of powerful antioxidants, as are dark-green leafy vegetables, such as spinach, kale and broccoli which are particularly good for boosting your immune system. Avocados are high in potassium and several B vitamins. Asparagus, onions, mushrooms, cucumber, peppers broccoli and several other green leafy vegetables deliver vital vitamin C as well as being powerful antioxidants, and are vital for ensuring the immune system functions properly as well as reducing the risk of developing Alzheimer's disease and memory loss.

The cruciferous family of vegetables includes cauliflower, cabbage, kale and other dark-green leaves containing vitamin K1, which is needed for a healthy metabolism and for efficient blood clotting.

Nature's vegetable harvest provides everything you need for your body and mind to function at optimum level. It delivers vitamins and minerals in the form that your body is best able to assimilate, without a supplement in sight.

Every time you prepare a meal for yourself, look for the colours of the rainbow on your plate, or in your lunch box, and you really can't go far wrong. When you think how beige your food choices used to be, and how deadened you felt after you had eaten them, you will love your technicolour meals and how well they make you feel and think.

Carli's kitchen story

My interest in eating paleo initially began because I'd just started strength/kettlebell training with Wonder Woman Workshops UK and they held a nutrition event which advocated a primal/paleo'ish diet and lifestyle. It really inspired me and I haven't looked back.

Eating real food is so easy. I've never eaten so much delicious food and there's nothing I desperately miss from my old way of eating. I like trying out new recipes to keep things varied and interesting. Another good tip is taking the time to dress a salad or vegetables properly. I generally use a tablespoon of olive oil with a teaspoon of apple cider vinegar or balsamic vinegar with salt and pepper. Then I get stuck in with my hands to swirl everything around to ensure it's all covered – such a simple thing but makes a world of difference to the taste.

One of my favourite recipes is making my own Scotch eggs, and using anchovies when I cook lamb is amazing. When I'm in a hurry I usually have oven-baked sea bass cooked with lime, chilli and coriander as it takes about 20 minutes from prep to table. I also usually have lots of different beef, lamb or turkey burgers that I've batch prepared and keep in the freezer. I'll happily eat those for breakfast, lunch or dinner.

A smoothie is also another great time saver in the morning. I usually have some berries and bananas in the freezer and then I'll add in some spinach, protein powder and cinnamon. The most important thing is ensuring you have some healthy ingredients that you can throw something together with or some pre-prepared food in the freezer. Making a hash from leftover vegetables and potatoes is also a favourite – grated sweet potato, red onion, bacon, kale and fresh sage is a particularly tasty combination.

My kitchen cupboard would not be complete without herbs and spices – dried, frozen and fresh. I try to get lots into most meals as they have amazing health benefits: full of antioxidants; anti-inflammatory; help digestion; regulate blood sugar, etc. Plus they make food really delicious. My current top three favourites are turmeric, cinnamon and smoked paprika.

For lunch at work I usually box up leftovers from the previous evening. I quite often cook extra and it just makes life a little bit easier. Snacks tend to be spiced chicken goujons, macadamia nuts, boiled eggs, bone broth, berries, occasionally a Scotch egg, or mashed banana with cinnamon and a pinch of salt. I'm also trying to eat more fermented foods so will add in some sauerkraut too.

My current favourite meal is spiced pulled lamb. It takes a bit of preparation to marinade the shoulder of lamb but once that is done it goes into the slow cooker for the day. The meat just falls apart and is so delicious. It also means I have plenty left over for a lot of lunches.

For tonight's dinner I'm making my own chicken Kiev with bacon, garlic and parsley butter. I use ground almonds and smoked paprika for the coating instead of breadcrumbs. I'll serve it with a baked sweet potato with herby leeks, courgette and kale.

Since I've been eating real food I've noticed I have more energy and I don't really have that terrible afternoon slump any more. It's not just about the food, I've also made an effort to reduce my stress; spend more time with family and friends and just have more fun. I'm still a work in progress but I've definitely made a lot of positive changes in my life beyond just my plate.

The words of encouragement I would offer someone beginning to explore feeling differently about food is to not to be too hard on yourself. If you have something to eat that isn't considered to be pukka 'real food' then just get back on track at the next meal.

I've become quite evangelical about this way of eating and how much better one can feel insofar that I've taken the plunge and I'm currently training in nutrition. I plan to make this the focus of next stage in my career. I already know it's going to be my life's passion which is very exciting.

You can follow Carli on Face Book http://fb.me/calilouan or her website www.carlilouan.com

Swapping old for new

Swapping what you usually eat for a healthier alternative is a great way to boost your nutritional levels and the quality of what you are eating. There is no need to feel you are missing out and some of these alternatives could soon become your favourite choices too. The philosophy of *How to Feel Differently about Food* is not about depriving yourself of food or going hungry, or going without, but of adding in new and exciting food choices to your meals that are satisfying and tasty.

Pasta and noodle swap for veg-etti

Courgettes (zucchini) sliced finely are a tasty alternative to ribbon pasta, such as fettuccine, or to lasagne pasta sheets. Use a vegetable peeler to slice the courgette into ribbons or buy a spiraliser to make coils that are shaped like spaghetti. They taste great with a home-made beef Bolognese sauce. You will need about six good-sized courgettes for a serving for two to three people. Alternatively, you can spiralise sweet potatoes instead of courgette or mix the two vegetables together. For extra convenience, supermarkets are beginning to sell pre-prepared spiralised vegetables. Lightly fry them in olive oil or coconut oil for a few minutes prior to serving.

Popular in America, spaghetti squash is a type of pumpkin which is becoming more widely available in the UK. The insides of this vegetable make a wonderful low-carbohydrate alternative to traditional pasta. Just cut open the squash and scoop out the insides. Fry lightly as explained above.

All of these swaps provide extra portions of healthy vegetables with your meal. By contrast to nutrient-poor white or wholewheat pasta, they provide several B vitamins as well as vitamins C, E and K. The orange-coloured vegetables are also a good source of essential minerals, including calcium, zinc, copper, magnesium and selenium, though levels of these vary depending on the soil in which the crop has been grown. Modern agriculture often leaves the soil denuded of trace minerals so if your budget runs to it, consider buying organic vegetables. Organic or biodynamic farming methods follow crop rotations and natural ways of enriching the soil that lend themselves to higher levels of these vital trace elements.

Dairy swapped for almond, hazelnut, hemp or coconut milk

Many people watching their waist-line choose skimmed milk. This highly processed product has to have synthetic vitamins added to replace those removed in processing. It is nutrient-poor and is an ideal candidate to be swapped for any of the tasty and nutrient-dense milks made from nuts. Be aware that some manufacturers consider the term 'Original Recipe' to mean 'with added sugar', so avoid those; other nut milks have lots of additives including synthetic vitamins so, as with all packaged products, it is important to read the labels.

Pastry-case swapped for protein-rich nut crust

Swap pastry cases for quiches and flans with an alternative version made from ground-up nuts. Simply buy ground-up nuts or grind them at home in a food processor. Ground almonds (almond meal) makes a particularly tasty crust which has the added advantage, if you have a dietary requirement, of being gluten-free.

You will need 250 g/8 oz of ground almond (almond meal). Add in two or three chopped garlic cloves and fresh or dried herbs of your choice along with a little sea salt and ground black pepper. You'll need an oil to bind these ingredients together and for this you can use 200 ml of olive oil or melted ghee or coconut oil. Coconut oil works best for crusts that are to be used as part of a dessert as it has a milder flavour. Mix the dry ingredients with the melted fat and press into the base of a flan or pie dish and around the sides. There is no need to pre-cook the nut crust prior to using it with a filling of your choice. It works particularly well with four to six eggs mixed with pre-fried red onions, roasted peppers and small chunks of roasted butternut squash. This is an ideal dish for breakfast, brunch or supper with a dressed green salad drizzled with a good virgin olive oil and lemon juice.

Rice swapped for cauliflower rice

Use a whole head of cauliflower zapped in a food processor until it resembles fine white rice. No need to add extra water. Cover with microwave-approved cling film or food wrap and microwave on high for three minutes. It's then ready to eat as a healthy alternative to any dish instead of white or brown rice. Alternatively, it can be fried with a little olive oil or coconut oil with spices or herbs to complement your main course. It's delicious.

Cauliflower rice can also be pressed onto a baking sheet in the shape of a pizza base and toppings of your choice added so that you can enjoy the flavour of pizza without the usual doughy white-bread base.

Experiment and try out swaps of your own, ditching poor nutritional foods or ingredients for nutrient-rich, flavoursome alternatives. You'll be surprised how delicious these alternatives can be.

The 'snog', 'marry' or 'divorce' of foods

'Snog' – foods to eat in moderation (they're an occasional treat)
'Marry' – foods to embrace and enjoy
'Divorce' – foods to split-up from

Instead of red, amber or green traffic lights to depict foods to stop, treat with caution, or go with, we have taken the dating analogy and applied it to foods we suggest you embrace wholeheartedly, kiss and run from, or dump unceremoniously.

'Snog' – foods to eat in moderation

The snog list is for foods to keep your eye on. Just as with love, this list holds some surprises and some disappointments. Foods you may have thought would be endlessly good for you, may need to have tabs kept on them. Some of these can't be fully trusted for their nutritional quality and could actively undermine your quest for optimum health.

Alcohol
There are several benefits from taking a break from drinking alcohol, not least of which is the hoary old chestnut of 'Is it possible for me to go without having a drink for a while?' Well, this is your opportunity to find out. Drinking, as with eating, can be a habit you've developed for handling challenges in your life, or a way of masking your true moods and emotions. If it feels overwhelming to tackle your drinking levels on your own, we recommend you consider working with a therapist who is trained and experienced with issues around alcohol use. You can find accredited and registered therapists online or in local directories. Also in the UK, your local General Practitioner (GP) would be a good place to start to get the help you need.

The effects of drinking alcohol are legion. It puts pressure on the liver, can cause reduced fertility in both men and women, and is clearly linked to increased blood pressure and increased risk of developing various cancers and cardiovascular health problems, including increased risk of heart attacks.

Alcohol also negatively affects your ability to sleep well. Your body repairs itself while you sleep. When you drink in the evening and then go to bed the worse for wear, it's common to fall quickly into a deep sleep. This omits the natural first stage of sleep, called rapid eye movement, or REM, sleep. Sleeping sober you usually experience six or seven cycles of REM sleep so that when you awake in the morning you feel rested and refreshed. Sleeping after drinking alcohol reduces the cycles of REM sleep to one or two, and with that there is also a corresponding reduction in the deep-sleep phase of sleeping, all of which leaves you feeling physically, and mentally, under par. You can find out more about how to achieve improved sleep patterns in 'The sleeping cure' on page 15.

If poor sleep quality isn't enough of a problem for your body to cope with, the fact that alcohol is a diuretic practically guarantees your sleep will be broken with frequent visits to the bathroom.

Furthermore, alcohol is the perfect delivery system for your body to easily consume sugars. The higher the carbohydrate count in a drink, the higher the amount of sugars. All of which is at odds with eating and drinking foods that do not contain excess sugar.

Whatever you choose to drink, go for quality over quantity. It is very difficult to achieve improved physical and mental health and gain subtle personal insights into your natural rhythms and moods whilst surveying your life through the bottom of a glass.

You may find devising a future strategy for yourself with alcohol is beneficial. For most people it is not realistic, or even necessary, to abstain from drinking forever. However, you may find it easier not to drink at all on certain days of the week than manage to be self-limiting. Many people decide not to drink from Sunday to Thursday, and enjoy a drink or two on Friday and Saturday evenings, for instance. Nothing is irrevocable and you may well find that imposing a few boundaries on yourself around alcohol enables you to feel more in control. It's good to take this break from drinking to allow a little light to shine on to what may have gradually become an unhealthy habit – perhaps even one that has become more central to your life than you had realised or would wish.

Persevere with it! The more challenging having a break from drinking proves to be, the more worthwhile this can be for you.

Note: If you feel you have developed a physical dependency on alcohol, your withdrawal or even significant reduction can be particularly challenging and potentially dangerous to your health. It is important to ensure you have adequate medical support and advice if this is the case.

Coffee and tea

We often use caffeine to push our bodies to carry on when really we need to rest. The habitual use of coffee increases the production of stress hormones, which has the knock-on effect of increasing insulin production. This in turn sets in train a whole series of physical reactions in the body that are not wholly beneficial.

The vicious cycle caffeine can set up is to disrupt sleep, which in turn promotes anxiety and depression. It's a cliché of our modern age to be tired and yet at the same time wired and over-caffeinated. Nothing feels worse than those physically uncomfortable symptoms of coffee-jag.

If you drink a lot of coffee you might want to consider resetting your coffee habits by taking a break for a week or so and see what it feels like to live without this popular stimulant. Once you have got over the withdrawal symptoms, which can be quite severe including vomiting in extreme cases, you will be amazed how naturally energised you feel.

If you choose not to start your day with your usual morning coffee order, clearly you may miss the caffeine hit to begin with. However, you would be amazed to know how often people substitute drinking a coffee when they are actually hungry for real food. We encourage you to breakfast and snack wisely so that you do not let your blood sugar levels get too low and to substitute herbal teas for coffee. Instead of going 'cold-turkey' with coffee and facing potentially severe side effects an alternative is to gradually replace caffeine drinks with non-caffeine ones over the first few days so that by the end of the week you are caffeine free and mostly over any side effects. We also understand that most of us enjoy drinking coffee and tea too much to make it permanently *verboten*. However, we think it's always useful to reappraise the eating and drinking habits we take for granted, and that includes our beverages. It is after all our old eating and drinking habits that have influenced where we are today and making an appraisal is an opportunity to make improved choices.

Coffee gets bad press but the benefits of drinking coffee in moderation outweigh the perceived benefits of total abstinence as coffee has a very strong antioxidant capacity. If you switch from your usual milk and froth-laden latte or frappe concoction to organic coffee with a teaspoon of coconut oil, you'll be giving your body a healthy boost instead of loading up on lots of empty calories. (Coconut oil is a good quality fat that helps eliminate blood sugar spikes and troughs throughout the day.)

The morning milky coffee is part of some people's reward system for having a tough and challenging day ahead. This can be so important that the thought of giving it up feels like real deprivation. If you are such a person, we understand the power of comfort foods to help you through tough times. We suggest you find new and more positive ways to reward yourself instead of consuming something that could be stalling the optimum health you want to achieve. Try swapping your usual milky coffee for a freshly made green smoothie. Alternatively you can opt out all together and decide to save the extortionate cost of coffee-chain drinks and buy yourself a magazine or a beauty/grooming product like a face pack to use later in the bath.

Tea is not dissimilar to coffee in that we recommend you go organic when you can and not adulterate the antioxidants found in both drinks with dairy or sugar, especially as dairy binds to antioxidants and makes them no longer bio-available. Go pure. Go fancy. Raise your game and choose quality.

Dairy
Dairy products (milk, cheese, yoghurt and so on) are a common cause of digestive issues for many adults and are worth avoiding if they cause you problems. The reason to avoid dairy is the body not being able to absorb or digest either the protein component of milk (casein) or the sugar component (lactose). Intolerance symptoms can range from mild to severe

and include:

Bloating

Flatulence, wind

Diarrhoea

Skin conditions

Stomach cramps

Rhinitis and sinusitis – the reason opera singers avoid milk.

Foggy brain from the morphine form of partially digested casein

In addition, both lactose (the sugar found in milk) and the growth hormones that are naturally in milk (baby animals need to grow) potentially cause weight gain.

In its most severe form, symptoms of lactose intolerance are similar to those of coeliac disease.

If you are avoiding dairy products, be aware that other less obvious milk-derived ingredients are concealed in pre-prepared foods with names such as:

- Acidophilus milk
- Ammonium caseinate
- Buttermilk powder
- Calcium caseinate
- Casein
- Delactosed whey
- Demineralised whey
- Hydrolysed casein
- Iron caseinate
- Lactalbumin
- Lactoferrin
- Lactoglobulin
- Lactose
- Lactulose
- Magnesium caseinate
- Potassium caseinate
- Recaldent
- Rennet casein
- Sodium caseinate
- Sweet whey
- Whey powder
- Whey protein concentrate
- Whey protein hydrolysate
- Zinc caseinate

You'll need to steadfastly read labels on prepackaged foods and drinks or, better still, avoid them altogether.

If you are avoiding cows' milk you can buy other milks made from various nuts. Choose the ones with the least sugar which will be shown on the label by the amount of carbohydrates contained in 100 ml. The most commonly available nut milks are almond, cashew and hazelnut milk. Almond milk is particularly high in protein, vitamin E and magnesium, which is a boon for bone strength.

If you can eat dairy products without the symptoms listed, yoghurt can be a good source of nutrition, but there are so many brands of yoghurt available these days it is difficult to know what is beneficial. Although most are flavoured, low-fat or fat-free, your goal is to find unflavoured, full-fat (at least 10 per cent), preferably live or pro-biotic varieties as these will provide far more nutrients and be much better for you and your digestive system. You are looking for brands with the least ingredients, no sweeteners, sugars (including 'skimmed-milk powder') or thickening agents. Avoid buying low-fat yoghurts as they will most likely have all of those ingredients included in an attempt to make them more palatable.

Calcium is essential for strong bones and teeth. It is only full-fat raw organic milk and yoghurt that are a useful source of calcium If milk has been pasteurised the calcium is no longer 'bio-available' to our digestive system. Greater levels of bio-available calcium can be found in green vegetables, the darker the better.

Fruit

A little-known fact is that you can eat too much fruit. The five-a-day slogan was not created by a nutritionist but by the fruit lobby to increase sales. It has no basis in enhancing health whatsoever. So, should you eliminate fruit from your diet? No. Eating small amounts of whole fruits is good.

When we eat foods high in the sugar glucose, insulin is released which lets the brain know when we've had enough to eat. High insulin levels then quell the appetite.

Fruit contains the sugar fructose, however, which doesn't stimulate the release of insulin or of leptin – the hormone that makes you feel full – so theoretically you could eat excessive quantities of fruit without feeling satisfied. Furthermore, our bodies don't have much use for fructose so excessive amounts end up being stored in the liver and pancreas where they can cause health problems such as non-alcoholic fatty liver disease. If you receive your fructose only from eating fruit and vegetables (where it originates), as most people did a century ago, you'd consume about 15 grams a day. Today the average consumption is around 70+ grams per day, which is 500 per cent higher, and our bodies simply cannot tolerate the increase. Carefully consider the fruits based on the list below and try to keep your fructose intake to below 15-20 grams per day.

To get the most fruit benefits for your buck, we recommend berries as being tasty and appealing and comparatively low in fructose. And remember, when you read 'fructose', think 'sugar' because that is what it is. (You can read the sugar entry in the 'foods to split-up from' list (page 86) to find out more about fructose, and how human beings are genetically predisposed to store even the smallest quantities of it as fat.) The higher the fructose score here the greater the caution with which you should treat these fruits and limit them in your food choices.

Limes	1 medium	0 grams of fructose
Lemons	1 medium	0.6 grams of fructose
Cranberries	1 cup	0.7 grams of fructose
Passionfruit	1 medium	0.9 grams of fructose
Prune	1 medium	1.2 grams of fructose
Guava	2 medium	2.2 grams of fructose
Date (Deglet noor)	1 medium	2.6 grams of fructose
Cantaloupe	1/8 slice	2.8 grams of fructose
Raspberries	1 cup	3.0 grams of fructose
Clementine	1 medium	3.4 grams of fructose
Kiwi fruit	1 medium	3.4 grams of fructose
Blackberries	1 cup	3.5 grams of fructose
Star fruit	1 medium	3.6 grams of fructose
Cherries, sweet	10	3.8 grams of fructose
Strawberries	1 cup	3.8 grams of fructose
Cherries, sour	1 cup	4.0 grams of fructose
Pineapple	1 slice 9 x 2 cm	4.0 grams of fructose
Grapefruit, pink or red	½ medium	4.3 grams of fructose
Boysenberries	1 cup	4.6 grams of fructose
Tangerine/mandarin/orange	1 medium	4.8 grams of fructose
Nectarine	1 medium	5.4 grams of fructose
Peach	1 medium	5.9 grams of fructose

Orange (navel)	1 medium	6.1 grams of fructose
Papaya	½ medium	6.3 grams of fructose
Honeydew	1/8th slice	6.3 grams of fructose
Banana	1 medium	7.1 grams of fructose
Blueberries	1 cup	7.4 grams of fructose
Date (medjool)	1 medium	7.7 grams of fructose
Apple	1 medium	9.5 grams of fructose
Persimmon	1 medium	10.6 grams of fructose
Watermelon	1/16th	11.3 grams of fructose
Pear	1 medium	11.8 grams of fructose
Raisins	¼ cup	12.3 grams of fructose
Grapes, seedless red or green	1 cup	12.4 grams of fructose
Mango	½ medium	16.2 grams of fructose
Apricots, dried	1 cup	16.4 grams of fructose
Figs, dried	1 cup	23.0 grams of fructose

Of all the fruits, we recommend blackberries and raspberries among our favourites to include every day. A small portion of either fresh or frozen makes a great dessert that tastes positively luxurious. If you are including dairy, then serve with a dessert spoonful of full-fat Greek yoghurt, or a dash of cream topped with a sprinkling of ground nuts, pumpkin seeds and linseeds. All berries are chock full of dietary fibre and are a wonderful source of antioxidants.

Nightshades family
The nightshade family of foods is made up of peppers (bell, chilli etc), aubergine (eggplant), tomatoes and potatoes. This group of vegetables contains small amounts of poisonous glycoalkaloids called tomatine, solanine and chaconine. You may or may not be sensitive to these chemicals.

Nightshades have a reputation as contributing to a number of chronic conditions, such as arthritis, fibromyalgia, IBS and gout. Members of this family may look as though they have little in common but in botanical terms they are related, and historically none was considered edible, because some related varieties, such as 'deadly nightshade', were known to be highly poisonous. Today, the standard American diet (SAD) includes many members of the nightshade family. The most popular, of course, is the white potato. They are chipped, roasted or baked, and eaten without a second thought practically each and every day, and often served with tomato ketchup. Tomatoes, another member of the nightshade family, are in every Bolognese sauce, either shop-bought or home-made.

More scientifically led research needs to be undertaken to assess the impact of eating from the nightshade family and the long-term effects on health. In the meantime, most people do not worry about eating white potatoes but they do know not to eat potatoes that are green, or are sprouting, as they can cause stomach upset or gastrointestinal problems. The body may in fact be responding to a higher level of glycoalkaloid present in the improperly stored or sprouting potatoes. Eating those for a person with a healthy digestive tract will mostly just cause some short-term discomfort but for someone with an already compromised gut, it could cause serious disruption to their health.

You will have an awareness of your own health challenges, and whether the sacrifice of avoiding the nightshade family could benefit you. You will probably find out more conclusively, and certainly more quickly, by noting changes for yourself rather than waiting for science to do the research for you. It should be enough just to remove all the members of the nightshade family from your diet for a few weeks to see if you feel better.

Nuts and seeds
There are a couple of reasons to be wary of eating or snacking on nuts. For one, it's very easy to go overboard and just keep eating them. Remember we are aiming to achieve a balance of healthy nutrition, and over-indulging in nuts and seeds eaten in excess can make this difficult. A useful way to manage consumption is to decant larger bags into smaller-sized servings. Take a small bag of nuts and seeds out with you, and once they're gone, they're gone. Or, you can buy nuts and seeds in their shells. The whole process of shelling and manoeuvring the edible part out of the shell helps to slow down consumption.

Nuts also contain small amounts of gut irritants which can lead to gut inflammation, called 'saponins'. They also contain 'anti-nutrients' called 'phytates', which inhibit the absorption of vitamins and minerals.

It is thought that nuts and seeds contain these unfavourable elements to discourage birds and other wildlife from eating them in their natural habitat. If they are eaten they are quickly passed through the digestive system and expelled.

This indigestible phytate content can be radically reduced by soaking nuts and seeds overnight in water and then drying them out at a low temperature in the oven before eating them.

Salt aka table salt, aka sodium chloride

Our bodies do need a small amount of salt to survive but salt intake has risen considerably over the last 50 years and is thought to be a major contributor to many modern diseases, including raised blood pressure which increases the risk of heart attacks, heart failure and strokes.

Current dietary advice from World Action on Salt & Health (2016) acknowledges that almost everyone in the Western world eats too much salt. In the UK it is recommended that an adult should not consume more than 6 grams a day (equivalent to a teaspoon) compared with the average salt intake which is currently 8.1 grams of salt a day, with many people exceeding even this.

It may not be enough just to cut down or omit sprinkling salt on your food at the table, although of course that would be a useful strategy, but it will not solve the problem that a high proportion of the salt consumed is hidden. To really take yourself into the realm of consuming lower levels it is important to cut out the main offender for hidden salt which is processed foods. You will need to read the nutritional label to see how much salt is in a serving portion or 100 grams. To add to the complication, salt is not always called 'salt'. Labels often list 'sodium' instead. This can be misleading as sodium amounts can seem small when compared with salt quantities but for accurate salt levels it is necessary to multiply the sodium amount by 2.5 – that is, one gram of sodium per 100 grams of a food equals 2.5 grams of salt per 100 grams.
Some surprising foods can also be high in salt, from bread and biscuits to breakfast cereals, as well as canned soup, oven-ready pizzas, ready meals and

some cheeses, so it is important to check salt levels before you buy, or take back control by preparing your own fresh ingredients. Try cooking without adding salt and be aware that it is perfectly possible to eat tasty food without the addition of any salt by cooking with garlic, herbs, spices etc instead.

Salt is an acquired taste so be aware of how much salt you sprinkle on your meals. Just like cutting down on sugar, your taste buds can quickly adjust to less salt and you can reap the health benefits too.

The Consensus Action on Salt and Health (CASH) destroys the myth that gourmet salts, such as rock and sea salts, are better for you. These often expensive artisan salts are just as damaging to your health as regular salt, despite claims that the products are natural and contain minerals. However, artisan salts are free of sodium aluminosilicate, a man-made anti-caking agent which is present in many commercial table salts. It is incorporated to encourage the highly processed tiny grains of salt to be free-flowing.

'Marry' – foods to embrace and enjoy

The 'marry' foods are those you can trust. Embrace them. Enjoy them. They are lifetime partners for you.

Bone broth
Bone broth has been shown to improve digestion, reduce allergies and boost immune health as well as having other health benefits. It is made by boiling beef, chicken or fish bones, depending on your preference. Always choose high-welfare bones from grass-fed beef, free-range chicken or wild, un-farmed fish where possible as they will be exposed to less, or preferably no, chemical pollution, growth hormone etc and will provide the greatest health benefits. Paleo fans swear by this mineral-rich stock made from slow-cooking the bones in water. The larger the bones the longer you'll need to simmer them so that they completely break down and release their nutrients. Chicken bones will need to simmer for up to 24 hours while fish bones will only need eight hours. Beef bones need to cook down for a seriously long time; it is not unusual to have a pot gently simmering away for 48 hours or more. The

resulting infusion is rich in minerals known to boost the immune system; improve digestion; relieve allergies; and even aid brain health by improving cognitive ability. The slow cooking breaks down the bones to release collagen so bone broth also helps to support joint flexibility and hair growth, improves skin tone and strengthens nails.

Once made, it can be frozen in serving sizes to be incorporated into soups, stews and sauces, or a glass of broth can be drunk each day. It is also helpful to have broth on hand when anyone in the family feels unwell and loses their appetite. It can be a soothing and immune-boosting drink to speed recovery.

Here is how to make bone broth for yourself.

> *Place about ½ to one kilogram (1-2 lb) of beef bones, purchased from an organic butcher, or the leftover carcass of a free-range, organic chicken, together with a splash of organic apple-cider vinegar, a few root vegetables, chopped or crushed garlic, a couple of chopped onions, and a handful of fresh herbs into a large saucepan.*
>
> *Cover with cold water. Bring to the boil and then simmer with a close-fitting lid over a very low heat for several hours until the bones have disintegrated. An ideal cooking pot is an electric slow-cooker as it can be set to cook at a very low temperature and left just to get on with it for hours. Top up with fresh water if required.*
>
> *Strain the liquid and discard any debris.*
>
> *It is important to cool down the broth quickly. It will keep fresh in the fridge for a couple of days, or freeze into serving portions.*

You can buy pre-made bone broth in cartons, but as with so many store-bought products, it is important to determine provenance, whether it is organic or not and what level of salt (sodium chloride) it contains; buy the lowest salt content available.

Chocolate

Firstly, not all chocolate is equal. Not all 'chocolate' is even principally made of chocolate. 'Chocolate' from some of the most popular UK household brands did not, until quite recently, meet the European Union (EU) criteria to be even called chocolate. Only a few years ago there was finally a conclusion to a long battle to redefine what chocolate was before some UK brands were legally available for sale in the EU without the stigma of being labelled as 'chocolate substitute'. These UK brands use cheaper vegetable fat (including hydrogenated coconut or palm oils) and the cocoa solids may be mixed with cheaper ingredients too; the lack of chocolate flavour is compensated for by the addition of extra sugar.

We recommend you buy chocolate that is made with a percentage of cocoa above 70 per cent. It's usually marked quite clearly on the packaging. If you are new to good-quality dark chocolate, be prepared to be surprised, as it can pack a strong bitter taste, when compared with the milk chocolate you may be used to eating. It is worth persevering with and getting used to the taste as dark chocolate is packed with beneficial organic compounds, including polyphenols and flavonols among others. Dark chocolate may also improve the function of the brain; one study of healthy volunteers showed that five days of consuming high-flavonol cocoa improved blood flow to the brain and cocoa may also significantly improve cognitive function in elderly people with mental impairment (Desideri et al, 2012).

Just one or two squares a day of good-quality, dark chocolate impart many health benefits, including a reduction in your chances of heart failure, and can help to lower your blood pressure as well.

Eggs

We debunk the myth that you need to limit your egg intake in the section called Master your breakfasts (page 41) and, in particular, Start your day with an egg (page 44). We hope that with this new knowledge you will now be persuaded to confidently include eggs in your meals on a regular basis. Eggs are one of the cheapest sources of high-quality protein you can buy, so buy the best quality you can afford. Also, do not just think of eggs as a breakfast food; you can have them hard-boiled with a Greek salad along with feta cheese, and olives, or made into a quick and easy omelette in a matter of moments, or served with a green salad for a quick supper too.

Fermented foods

A key way to optimise levels of stomach acid and healthy digestive enzymes is to include fermented foods in your regular diet. They can improve gut health, which is linked to healthy weight loss and to enhanced mental health. The practice of fermenting foods goes back hundreds of years as a means of preserving fruit, vegetables and fish for lean times.

The most common fermented food is probably yoghurt, so make sure you buy a good-quality, live, plain, full-fat variety. (If you are avoiding cows' milk, goat and sheep milk yoghurts may be available, and coconut yoghurt is a delicious alternative to all milk-related yoghurts.) There are other, less well known, fermented drinks, such as kefir made from milk (it can also be water-based) or kombucha, which is fermented from tea. Both are available from health stores. Buy the one with the least ingredients and without added sugars.

Be aware, however, that unfortunately some people cannot tolerate fermented foods as they are susceptible to the high levels of nitrogen-containing organic compounds called 'biogenic amines'. These can be a known trigger for headaches and migraines. You may need to experiment and find out what works for you. After all, even the humble olive is a fermented food so it might be easy and palatable to just include a few olives as a pre-dinner appetiser.

A wide variety of vegetables can be fermented at home. The most common is cabbage, which is very simple to ferment and you may know this as 'sauerkraut'. It can be eaten like a pickle to add healthy enzymes to your meals.

Take one head of cabbage, either green or red, or bok choy, or perhaps a combination of all three.

Cut into thin strips and sprinkle with a good quality sea salt. Massage the salt into the cabbage until the cabbage wilts and produces a salty liquid (brine). This can take some time.

Drain off the brine and reserve this liquid.

Sterilise a wide-neck jar with boiling water.

Pack the cabbage tightly into the sterilised jar. Once the jar is almost full pour the reserved brine back over the cabbage until it is covered. (You may have to add more salt water to ensure the cabbage is properly covered.) Submersion is important to avoid mould growing on the top layer. This can be achieved by weighting down your vegetables with a stone; one from your garden that you've run through the dish washer will do, or alternatively if you're using a wide-neck jar find another jar that fits inside the rim of the one holding your fermenting vegetables. The top jar can be weighted with more stones or baking pie weights.

Check on the fermentation every couple of days. Remove any mould that has grown and push back down with a fork any cabbage that has emerged from the brine.

The flavour increases over time. It should be at its peak, between three weeks and a month.

Also try experimenting with other vegetables.

Shop-bought fermented vegetables, including cabbage, are available from health-food stores. Just check the label for ingredients and buy unpasteurised where possible to ensure maximum beneficial live enzymes.

Fibre

According to the NHS (UK National Health Service) many adults do not get enough fibre. On average, most people in the UK consume about 18 grams of fibre a day. That is only just over half of the recommended minimum of 30 grams a day (NHS Choices, 2015).

Fibre is only found in fruit and vegetables and does not exist in meat, fish and dairy. It comes in in two forms – soluble fibre and insoluble fibre – and both types are essential for a healthy digestive system. For instance, the skin of a sweet potato is insoluble fibre that can't be digested by your body. It passes through your digestive system and helps other food move through your gut more efficiently to maintain bowel health. (If you have a digestive disorder such as IBS (irritable bowel syndrome) your symptoms may be affected by the amount of fibre in your diet and you will need to be observant about what amount in your diet best suits you.) Other sources of insoluble fibre include wholemeal bread, bran, cereals, nuts and seeds (except golden linseeds).

The orange flesh of a sweet potato is a good example of soluble fibre. It can be digested by your body and it can help you feel fuller for longer. Soluble fibre helps by drawing fluids from your body to add bulk to your stool, helping to regulate how often and how easily you find it to eliminate waste. If you suffer from constipation you can alleviate this by gradually increasing the amount of soluble fibre in your diet until you achieve a regular pattern of passing stools that feels natural to you.

Other examples of soluble fibre include cereals, such as oats, barley and rye, bananas and apples, root vegetables, including carrots and parsnips, and seeds, including golden linseeds. Increasing the levels of soluble fibre consumed should be accompanied by drinking increased amounts of water, which will also be helpful in resolving constipation. (See Water, page 85.)

There are simple ways to gradually increase the amount of fibre you eat each day:
Choose whole fruits and vegetables instead of juice.

Make a green smoothie instead of a green juice – a smoothie maker incorporates all the fibre from the vegetables and fruit while a juicer separates out the beneficial fibre to leave just the liquid.

Eat a raw salad or a serving of home-made vegetable soup every day.

If you're eating bread, choose a whole-grain, artisan loaf made from ancient grains such as spelt flour. Alternatively, buy bread with added seeds and nuts.

Fresh or frozen berries, such as raspberries, make an ideal dessert and are a rich source of fibre.

When buying foods with nutritional labels check the fibre levels when comparing brands.

Eat raw carrots and celery crudités with a humus dip.

Finally, it is worth noting that experiencing constipation can impact negatively on your mood and can be a factor in feeling under par and depressed. Along with feeling physically unwell, constipation often causes a loss of appetite, a depletion of energy, irritability and increased unhappiness from the accompanying stomach pain and discomfort. Gently increasing your intake of fibre, which for most adults means almost doubling current consumption levels, can be beneficial to your digestive health and can also improve mood and general wellbeing.

Lemons

Lemon juice in warm water is a great way to start the day. Squeeze half a fresh lemon into warm water and drink. Do not use hot water as you want to preserve the lemon's natural antibacterial, antiviral and immune-boosting components, and its vitamin C. Starting the day this way can become a habit you really value and notice the benefits of. The sharp, citrus freshness of lemons also helps you to retrain your tastebuds away from desiring excessive sweetness. (Reduce the risk of lemon juice eroding tooth enamel by drinking it diluted as we recommend and avoid brushing your teeth with toothpaste immediately after consuming a lemon drink.)

Red meat

Standard, modern food choices make it more difficult to achieve the healthy levels of mono-unsaturated and omega-3 fats that we need in order to decrease the probability of developing a number of degenerative diseases and to make reductions in the incidence of cancer, diabetes and neurological impairment. This is due, in the main, to the way livestock is now raised unnaturally on grain feed instead of being free to graze on pasture. Modern farming methods' reliance on intensive production and dependence on pharmacology reduce the nutrients and beneficial fats found in both our cuts of meat and our dairy products.

Buying organic, free-range, pasture-grazed meat, dairy and eggs and wild game and fish isn't a fad. It is the only way to return to the range of nutrients and the healthy quantities of fats required for optimum health and nutrition. It will cost more, so eat less of it, or experiment with cheaper cuts of meat, which benefit from longer, slower cooking.

As said, beef ideally should be pasture-raised or grass-fed. This is because modern-day farmers have been forced to compete in a highly competitive international market place and to lower their standards of animal husbandry to survive. Cattle are increasingly kept in large sheds and fed grain instead of being raised outdoors. They often stand in their own excrement and so need higher levels of antibiotics to help them fight infection caused by their unnatural environment.

If pasture-raised meat is outside your budget, choose to eat lamb as farmers haven't yet found a way to raise sheep entirely on concrete. You can therefore be pretty sure it has grazed on some real grass for at least part of its life. Lamb joints can be expensive to buy; however, the cheaper cuts of lamb, such as breast or stewing lamb, lend themselves to slow cooking and are very tasty.

Pork needs to be free-range and high welfare. Do not buy cheap as it won't be either of these things. Pigs have the intelligence of an inquisitive two-year-old and often experience a miserable existence, from birth to death, kept indoors in sheds and raised on grain in a tiny space. It's not what you would want to eat, and neither are they farming methods you would want to support if you care about yourself or other animals. Look out too for supermarket-sold 'basted' pork and equivalents too, where water and dextrose (corn sugar) have been added to give inferior pork more flavour. As ever, be cautious and read labels.

It's the same with chicken. It is not possible to buy cheap chicken without recognising that it is a massive quality compromise and perpetuates a type of intensive farming that is at best inhumane. Chickens suffer serious physical and psychological discomfort when kept in overcrowded conditions. They cannot express their natural behaviours. They are unable to move around to forage for food and grubs, and their ability to dust-bathe and perch is either restricted or impossible. Buy free-range and organic chicken wherever possible.

Check the internet for money-saving offers from independent farmers selling grass-fed, free-range or pasture-raised meat. Working direct to the public, the farmers can often pass on price savings and undercut supermarket prices.

Fish
Look out for fish that is wild, not farmed, and preferably line-caught; it is best bought and eaten fresh on the same day.

Choose an oily fish over white fish. The most nutritional fish choices are wild salmon, mackerel, sardines, trout and sea bass. Salmon can be fresh or smoked. Find a fishmonger who will fillet and prepare the fish for you. They are often more than willing to offer advice on cooking different fish too.

Most fish cook in just a few minutes in a pan with a little butter, or steamed in the oven in a parcel made with baking paper or *en papillote* as the French call it. The joy of fresh fish is like a well-kept secret, and you can grow to love including it in a couple of your weekly meals.

Tinned fish, such as mackerel or sardines in olive oil, make a tasty, quick and sustaining snack spread thickly on a toasted slice of sourdough bread, for example.

Nuts and seeds
Nuts and seeds feature on the 'avoid' and the 'marry' lists simultaneously. So why is that?

A small handful of hazelnuts, almonds or macadamia nuts will make an excellent, nutritious snack. They are a good alternative source of protein too.

Do not choose peanuts or cashew nuts as they are not nuts at all but legumes (beans) which contain phytates as described on page 67. They are not as healthy as the true nuts (or 'tree nuts'), including walnuts, macadamias, hazelnuts, pecans and almonds.

The health advantage that nuts and seeds can provide is compromised by snacking on too many. Watch your portion size. Don't eat from an open packet; decant a few into a dish, or a small bag if you're taking them out with you so that way you can retain an awareness of how many you are eating. An ideal size serving of nuts is just the few nuts it takes to hold comfortably in the palm of your hand.

Vegetables

We are great fans of all vegetables and recommend you eat as wide a variety as you can of seasonal, preferably locally grown, and organic where possible. Try to buy the darkest green leafy vegetables available when you are offered a choice. The darker the green colour, the richer the source of minerals – including iron, calcium, potassium and magnesium – and vitamins – including K1, C, E and many of the B vitamins too. Try local markets or farmers' markets as an alternative to supermarkets for fresh supplies.

Sweet potatoes

Sweet potatoes are nutritionally far superior to white potatoes, packed as they are full of vitamins C, B3, B5, and B6, manganese, potassium and copper. The orange flesh is also a good source of soluble fibre, as we said earlier, which helps to keep you feeling fuller for longer while the skin is a useful source of insoluble fibre which can improve digestive problems such as constipation and diarrhoea. Even half a sweet potato a day will have a beneficial effect on bowel health for many people.

Sweet potatoes can be chipped, roasted, baked or mashed so can be swapped in many recipes that previously would have featured the humble white potato. Also, the sweet potato is botanically unrelated to the nightshades group of vegetables that includes the white potato. Therefore, for anyone adhering to the autoimmune protocol (eating plan to help address gut inflammation, page 116), the sweet potato makes both a nutritional and a more digestible alternative.

Fats and oils

The conventional wisdom regarding dietary fat, with the oft repeated mantra 'eat less saturated fat and more vegetable oil', has stood unchallenged since the late 1960s. Today, the same principles continue to be recommended by the Dietary Guidelines for Americans and are echoed in the UK Government's advice disseminated through the National Health Service (NHS) and specifically via the 'Eatwell Guidelines', updated in early 2016. It too persists in the dogma 'cut down on all fats and replace saturated fat with some unsaturated fat'.

The origins of this influential message began in Minnesota, where one of the world's largest and most rigorous experiments was tasked with answering the important question, 'How does eating fatty foods affect our health?' The real health implications of that research project have been obscured for over 50 years with potentially fatal consequences for hundreds of thousands of men and women who followed dietary guidelines designed to reduce their risk of heart disease that was, and is in real terms, unsupported by the massive trial.

The cracks in the research's conclusions became news in April 2016 when the *British Medical Journal* (BMJ) featured some never-before-published data that pushed the whole 'good fats' versus 'bad fats' debate onto the public stage with high-profile disagreements between international obesity charities and organisations as well as spats between senior medical professionals publicly disagreeing with each other and some even tendering their resignations.

So, what happened with the Minnesota Coronary Experiment all those years ago that could still reverberate through the decades and affect one of today's key public health messages? The original research cohort was literally thousands of institutionalised mental health patients who were divided into two groups to compare the effects of two diets. One group was fed a special diet containing less saturated fat, less cholesterol and more vegetable oil designed to lower blood cholesterol levels and reduce heart disease. The other group was fed a more typical American diet.

As the researchers predicted, the special diet group did reduce blood cholesterol. This result in itself did *not* seem to have any effect on heart disease outcomes, although the researchers *felt* confident that these benefits would have become apparent had the experiment continued for a longer period.

Now, with the benefit of hindsight, new research led by investigators from the US National Institute of Health and the University of North Carolina has shown that the incomplete publication of the original research contributed to erroneous conclusions being made all that time ago. Even more damning, Daisy Zamora, a leading author of the new analysis, concluded that the Minnesota Coronary Experiment overestimated the benefits and underestimated the potential risks of this special form of diet. She went on to say that had this research been published 40 years ago it might have changed the trajectory of diet-heart research and recommendations.

So, the debate about the most important question in nutrition goes on. 'Does the eating of saturated fats, typically found in meat and dairy, actually contribute to heart disease?' This is without doubt a very important question to resolve as the all-pervading belief has long been that the consumption of saturated fats is a leading cause of heart disease, which is in itself a leading cause of mortality in the US, the UK and the developed world in general.

The range of expert opinion is exemplified by Walter Willett, chair of the Nutrition Department at Harvard University, USA. He adheres to the accepted wisdom of the day and said in a blog post from the Medical School, '... this report adds no new information and is irrelevant to current dietary recommendations that emphasise replacing saturated fats with polyunsaturated.' A counter claim from Christopher Ramsden, a medical investigator at NIH in the US and also a leading author in the new analysis of the Minnesota Coronary Project's data, said the research suggested saturated fats 'may not be as bad as originally thought'.

So, how does this play out for ordinary consumers who want to eat real food to maximise their health and wellbeing? Zamora and Ramsden along with their other research colleagues discovered that some of the missing data from the original Minnesota Coronary Experiment did not properly evaluate the potentially harmful effects on human health of linoleic acid, which is found in most refined vegetable oils that are used as an alternative to saturated fats. Prior to the Second World War and the concomitant changes in farming and agricultural practices, linoleic acid was a mere bit-player in terms of human consumption and was only found in small quantities in the human diet. Fast forward to today and the standard American diet (SAD), and the diet of the Western world in general, is awash with highly processed vegetable and seed oils used for cooking every conceivable fast food, and added as an ingredient to cakes, ready meals, sauces, confectionary and an almost endless list of every type of processed food. The rise in the popularity of vegetable oils over animal fats can in large part be attributed to errors in the analysis of the Minnesota Coronary Experiment; the result is that humans are now consuming levels of linoleic acid that their bodies are not able to metabolise without harmful effects.

In conclusion, it seems it has never been scientifically proven that giving up saturated fats will make people healthier. Furthermore, repeated clinical trials and large-scale observational studies have even produced evidence to the contrary. At the same time, what does seem to be a vital consideration if you do cut saturated fats from your diet is what fats you replace them with.

Traditional fats and oils may after all be a better health option than modern, highly processed polyunsaturated seed and vegetable oils.

Choices to cook with
Every oil or fat has a 'smoke point'. It is the upper temperature limit to which an oil or fat can be heated without damage. Exceeding the smoke point means oxidation occurs in the fat, which begins to break down and release free radicals along with a substance called acrolein, which is the chemical responsible for the unpleasant bitter taste and smell of burnt food.

For cooking at high temperatures, such as frying, we recommend you choose a fat with a high smoke point of at least (205°C/400°F), such as beef tallow or clarified butter. For sautéing onions or chopped vegetables, we recommend you use a fat with a medium smoke point (165-190°C/325-375°F), such as virgin olive oil or duck or chicken fat.

For stir-frying with a neutral oil, we recommend coconut oil (175°C/350°F).

Choices to serve cold
Extra virgin olive oil, avocado oil or nut oils such as walnut or, even better, omega-3-rich macadamia nut oil, are great drizzled over salads and steamed vegetables.

Do not choose vegetable or seed oils. If you have them in your kitchen cupboard, please throw them away now. (These could be canola oil, rapeseed oil, soybean oil, sunflower oil, corn oil, cottonseed oil or safflower oil.) They are highly processed, unstable when heated and linked with many health issues.

Also throw away the 'healthy' spreads you may have bought that are advertised as an alternative to butter. The good news is you can enjoy butter again. (You can read more about this in the entry for margarines and 'spreads' in the 'Foods to split-up from' list on page 89.)

For many of you, being encouraged to eat more saturated or traditional oil and fats is going to feel counterintuitive when you want to lose weight. However, we have been very effectively brainwashed for over 50 years to cut down on all fats and increase our carbohydrate intake. We have been lied to. As part of eating as our grandmothers' generation would recognise, we encourage you to increase the amount of healthy fats you consume.

One of the most ancient sources of fat that is currently gaining in popularity in the West for its health-giving properties is coconut. The fat in coconut oil, cream and milk is made up of medium-chain fatty acids (MCFAs). The latest research shows that consuming coconut, in all its forms, promotes a healthy metabolism, helps us drop fat around the abdominal area, and supports healthy, successful weight loss.

Coconut oil is a healthy alternative to factory-made vegetable or seed oils as it has a high smoke point so you can cook with it at a high temperature without it burning. Coconut cream and milk are wonderful additions to your pantry, and can form the basis of many tasty and nutritious meals.

Butter is a much healthier option than any margarine or 'spread'. Butter from grass-fed herds is our preference. The Kerrygold brand of butter used to be made purely using milk from grass-fed cattle so was a good supermarket choice. They are changing their policy these days and incorporating a percentage of milk from non-grass-fed herds, but they remain a relatively good option until you can source/afford a less mass-market brand. The description to look for on the wrapper is 'Made from organic milk from grass-fed' or 'pasture-fed' cattle.

Butter and ghee are both good sources of vitamins A, D, K2 and E along with many other trace elements. Choose grass-fed or pasture-raised dairy for maximum benefits. Ghee has had the milk solids removed so has a much higher smoke point than butter, making it ideal for frying. In theory it is also an excellent option for people who are intolerant to milk sugar (lactose) or milk protein (casein) but traces of these may remain.

Coconut oil is a true wonder food, with many proven health benefits. It has a high smoke point and a clean taste, making it ideal for cooking uses, though some people do not like the faint taste of coconut. Just like olive oil, it comes in many quality levels. Look out for 'organic, cold-pressed' for the purest.

Nutritional yeast (fortified)
Nutritional yeast is a non-dairy alternative to cheese and is an option for those who are dairy intolerant. It is often thought to be a natural source of vitamin B12 but this is actually added in fortified brands. Nutritional yeast is also a useful source of iron, potassium, selenium, amino acids and other B vitamins, as well as providing the full set of essential amino acids, rarely found outside of red meat, so it is particularly useful to those following a vegetarian or vegan diet.

Spices and the power of micro-nutrients
Traditional cooking from the Indian subcontinent, the Far East and the Middle East uses far more spices than we do in the West. The spices used in these cuisines have been found to contain beneficial micronutrients that aid digestion and the production of healthy gut flora. The peoples of these hot climates eating these spicy foods have fewer digestive issues and a lower incidence of cancers of the stomach and bowel than their Western counterparts.

Unfortunately, it doesn't mean a Friday night takeaway from your local curry restaurant will do your digestion any discernible favours. Most commercially produced curry sauces are no longer made from freshly ground spices in individual restaurants but sold by a handful of distributors in bulk quantities of generic gunk. To maximise the health benefits of spicy food experiment at home to find ways to add spice and variety by incorporating some simple traditional Indian recipes in your own cooking. A good place to start would be Madhur Jaffrey's *An Invitation to Indian Cooking* and *Indian Vegetarian Cookery* by Jack Santa Maria. Both books featured in the *Observer Magazine*'s '50 Best Cookbooks of All Time' (2010). [Ref: Observer Food Monthly's expert team. 15 August 2010]

Cinnamon

Obtained from the bark of the *Cinnamomum verum* tree, cinnamon has through the ages been used for its antibacterial qualities. Modern science has confirmed eating cinnamon also significantly elevates the level of sodium benzoate in your brain. This causes a significant increase in a beneficial group of brain chemicals collectively described as 'neurotropic'. They are important in maintaining a healthy brain as well as preventing or slowing down the onset of degenerative brain diseases, such as Alzheimer's and Parkinson's disease.

Cinnamon has also been shown to reduce blood sugar levels in people with type II diabetes and can help reduce cholesterol levels by up to 25 per cent. So cinnamon can benefit your brain *and* body. Use it in coffee instead of sugar and sprinkle it on salads, desserts or cooked vegetables. It tastes wonderful with turmeric's golden milk featured opposite (page 85) (Wenk, 2010).

Garlic

Garlic is a powerful antioxidant you would be well advised to eat every day. Mince it, or use a garlic press, and add it your home-made virgin olive oil salad dressing, or add it whenever you are roasting meat or vegetables. It is antifungal and antiviral, when raw, and a good source of sulphur compounds which provide many helpful cardiovascular benefits. Aim for a whole head of garlic per week as a guideline.

Turmeric

Turmeric is an orange-coloured spice from India that has been widely used in Middle Eastern and Southeast Asian cooking for thousands of years. Ayurvedic and Chinese schools of medicine also utilise this wonderful spice to clear infections and inflammation on the inside and outside of the body.

Dr Randy J Horwitz wrote a paper for the American Academy of Pain Management in which he discussed the health benefits of turmeric and cited research published in 2006 (Funk et al). He stated that turmeric is one of the most potent anti-inflammatories available. This is great news for anyone seeking to heal the damage done to their bodies from over-consumption of sugar and carbohydrates.

A tasty and effective way to take turmeric is in a drink. It needs to be cooked first to ensure its beneficial properties are bio-available.

> *To make turmeric paste, gently heat half a cup of water (177 ml/6 fl oz) in a saucepan before adding a quarter of a cup (30 g/1oz) of turmeric powder.*
>
> *Stir gently over a low heat for seven to nine minutes, adding additional water as required to maintain a medium consistency.*
>
> *Once cooled it can be stored in a screw-top jar in the fridge and will keep for 14 days.*

This turmeric paste is the basis for making 'golden milk'.

> *Gently heat two cups of rice, almond or coconut milk, or dairy if you don't have a problem with it, with half a teaspoon to a whole teaspoon of the turmeric paste.*
>
> *You can add some freshly grated ginger as well.*
>
> *Warm it through gently and add a drizzle of almond or coconut oil with a good pinch of cinnamon.*
>
> *Drink daily.*

Water

It is in dispute how much water should be drunk per day for optimum health but it is a fact that most people are not drinking nearly enough. As a guideline, set yourself a target of eight tall glasses of water per day, or keep refilling an empty glass litre-bottle of water, and make sure you drink one bottleful in the morning, and one in the afternoon.

If you have lost the habit, never got the habit or are resistant to drinking pure water, then you can make it more palatable by chilling it in a glass jug in the refrigerator in the summer or warming it in the winter.

When the weather is chilly it's hard to get excited about drinking cold water so a wonderful alternative is a large mug of warm water with the juice of a freshly squeezed lemon or lime. Add a couple of slices of fresh ginger. If the water is too hot it destroys the enzymes in the lemon, reducing its nutritional benefits, so warm is best.

The slices of fresh ginger are a natural source of antimicrobial nutrients (they destroy germs and bugs), which is ideal, especially during the winter months. The lemon and lime help to make drinking water more palatable for some people and help your taste buds adjust to sharper, fresher tastes and away from the cloying, sweet tastes you might be more accustomed to.

When we speak to clients about increasing their water consumption they often complain that water is boring and ask if they can substitute it with something else. Sorry, the answer is no. The only way to naturally quench your thirst is by drinking life-sustaining water. It complicates and confuses your taste buds if your drinks are artificially sweetened or flavour-enhanced. Regular drinking of fresh water is a fundamental requirement for a healthy body and brain.

Do stick with this. If you struggle to find water appealing, then remember psychologists have worked out it takes 21 repetitions to embed a new habit so after just three weeks of drinking water it will seem like second nature.

'Divorce' – foods to split-up from

Here are the main food culprits to avoid. They have become so adulterated over the past 50 to 60 years or so that they are unrecognisable from their original, natural state.

The main criterion for placing foods on the avoid list is that they inflame your gut. As well as eating for nutrition we care very much about promoting gut health for the intrinsic health benefits that this can bring. Find out more about the role of gut health on page 116.

You probably already know many of these are not good for you but the good news is you aren't going to miss them when you have so many more wonderful foods to eat in their place. Clear them out of your life as efficiently as you can, from store cupboard to pantry – just ditch them!

Bread

Bread hasn't been the 'staff of life' for a long time. Mechanised baking methods relying on an assortment of additives and high-speed mixing, and modifications to wheat crops, have done nothing for bread. The modern-day loaf is unrecognisable from the bread of our grandmothers' day. Stodgy and bloat-inducing, it is full of sugar, salt and starchy carbohydrates.

Bread is increasingly linked to digestive issues and weight gain. Either go expensive with artisan bread made from a selection of organic flours using traditional, slow methods; home bake your own bread; or leave it out. The bread rolls given out at dinner to sailors in the Navy are nick named 'fat pills' and are avoided by the more able seamen.

If you want to continue to eat bread, experiment with artisan breads from specialist bakers. Spelt bread and other varieties made with ancient grains are becoming more widely available, as is sourdough bread that has been fermented slowly overnight. You may find eating a slice of toasted artisan bread with your morning eggs tastes wonderful and doesn't cause you any bloating.

Breakfast cereals

Controversially perhaps, we include muesli and granola here alongside those hundreds of different designs of corn processed and extruded into technicolour sugar-coated flakes, puffs and pops aimed at the children's breakfast market. Eaten with milk we consider even grown-up varieties to be a poor way to start your day. (You can read more in Master your breakfasts on page 41.) Muesli dresses up its dry and unappealing grains with masses of dried fruit, making for a huge fructose hit, while granola may sound like another healthy alternative except that it is loaded with sugar. Even the use of maple syrup does not make it healthy. (You can read more on the sugar entry for Maple syrup in the list of foods to avoid on page 94.)

Dairy

The consumption of traditional cows' milk products is not recommended for several reasons. They are a common gut irritant and can be the cause of constipation, as well as other gut issues. They are also the main culprit in promoting the production of mucus in the gut and in the respiratory tract. Dairy milk can also cause a spike in insulin levels that is disproportionate to the amount of sugar (lactose) it contains. There is evidence to support the theory that only around 35 per cent of adults the world over can produce the enzyme (lactase) essential for properly digesting milk sugar (Gerbault et al, 2011).

Instead of traditional dairy, consider milks made from nuts such as almonds. They are more readily available these days in supermarkets and are very palatable.

Milk and cheeses made from goats' milk contain fewer gut irritants and are more easily digested than products from cows' milk so are worth trying as an alternative.

Grain family

The wheat we eat today is unrecognisable from the wheat of even 50 years ago. In the last half century the way wheat is grown has fundamentally changed. It has been continually tinkered with to make it more resistant to pests and drought and to massively increase crop yields per acre. Farming has adopted hybrid seeds, man-made fertilisers, and ever more efficient pesticides.

The way wheat is milled also changed in the 1870s with the introduction of the modern steel roller mill replacing traditional stone ground milling. It was remarkably fast and efficient when compared with the old method. The new technology also provided for the first time finer and more accurate control over the various parts of the wheat kernel so that the portions that are richest in proteins, vitamins, lipids and minerals could be eliminated to produce pure white flour, a cheap food for the masses which had a much longer shelf-life than traditional flour.

It was applauded as a modern breakthrough and few people noticed the passing of wheat, formerly at the heart of humankind's diet for thousands of years, as it morphed into a 'fancy flour' denuded of any nutrients. Dr William Davis, the author of **Wheat Belly**, said: 'This thing being sold to us called wheat — it ain't wheat. It's this stocky little high-yield plant, a distant relative of the wheat our mothers used to bake muffins, genetically and biochemically light-years removed from the wheat of just 40 years ago' (Davis, 2011).

Many people today have a wheat allergy, or sensitivity, or avoid grains as they believe they are gluten intolerant even though they may have never had a medical diagnosis.

The grain family includes amaranth, barley, buckwheat, bulgur (cracked wheat), millet, oatmeal, oats, rice, rye, semolina and spelt. All of them to a lesser or greater extent have been modified in recent times, with the most popular grains receiving the most intervention As we consider grain products to be highly processed, in many cases we recommend you choose a more nutritious way to start your day than with a slice of toast or a bowl of cereal or muesli. We help you find some really easy and appetising alternatives in our Master your breakfasts on page 41.

Margarine and low-fat spreads

Most of the alternatives to butter sold in the chiller cabinet are pitched as a healthier alternative but are nothing more than an amalgam of over-heated fats, chemicals, additives and water spun together in laboratories. There is no healthy heritage for margarine or its ever-growing family of sibling spreads. They are all made of 'trans fats' which occur when vegetable oils (polyunsaturated fats) are 'hydrogenated' to make them solid but spreadable at room temperature. They are best avoided as they are known to contribute to the clogging of arteries and increasing levels of LDL (the cholesterol we don't want) while levels of HDL (the cholesterol we do want) decrease.

The rise in popularity of margarine and spreads in the last 50 or so years has been a food manufacturer's dream come true; it is a cheap product to produce that is sold at a premium price when it has the right list of additives. The advertising industry has been at its most compelling with its claims that rejecting butter in favour of these artificial products will aid health. Unfortunately, we've been sold a pup, and the tables are now turning as more and more health professionals recognise the true health value of butter or ghee over these impostors.

Shop-bought salad dressings

Don't buy manufactured salad dressings – make your own. Mix one of the great beneficial oils, such as virgin olive oil or avocado oil, with cider vinegar. (Look out for brands featuring 'The Mother ' on the label. This is an enzyme-rich sediment in the cider vinegar that aids digestion.)

The ratio for making a dressing is two parts oil to one part vinegar, or thereabouts. Play with flavours! Now you can add in plain yoghurt or minced garlic, some sea salt and black pepper, cinnamon, fresh herbs or any number of combinations. Mix it together in a jam-jar with a well-fitting lid and it will last for a couple of weeks in your fridge. If you make your own you will be spared the thickeners, dubious sweeteners, cheap toxic oils and fake flavourings in the shop-bought varieties.

Soya

Promoted as a healthy alternative to dairy, soya milk, and other soy products, are found in the chiller cabinets of health stores and supermarkets the Western world over. Fermented soy has been a staple of Asian cuisine since time immemorial but is not consumed in the form it is sold in in the West. Unfermented soy can disrupt hormone levels and it is recommended that people with any sort of thyroid or adrenal imbalance avoid soy because of this. Switch to an unsweetened almond milk or other nut-based milk instead. Soy sauce as a condiment to flavour food can be replaced with coconut aminos, which is similar to soy sauce in appearance and taste except it is slightly sweeter-tasting. This alternative is also free from the potential allergy triggers found in soy, or the wheat that standard soy sauce would contain. Health food shops stock coconut aminos plus they are becoming more widely available in large supermarkets.

Soda drinks and juices

Everyone is aware that drinking soda and cola-type drinks is not good for you. Today, the diet drinks are also coming under the spotlight as the artificial sweeteners they use in place of sugar still seem to play a part in obesity.

From early in life, the body develops a learned response to sweet tastes and expects a new intake of calories when a sweet taste stimulates the tongue's taste receptors. If this sweet taste is generated by sugar then at least some of the brain's needs for sugar are satisfied. However, if an artificial sweetener such as aspartame, or one of its growing list of contemporaries, is used to replace the sugar the outcome for the body is quite different. Aspartame was introduced into the beverage industry in the early '80s. As we already know, the sweet taste stimulates the tongue and the brain, and the stomach via the vagus nerve, then programs the liver to prepare to accept new energy from outside. In anticipation, the liver stops manufacturing sugar from the body's fat and glycogen reserves, storing them instead.

In the case of artificial sweeteners, the sweet taste doesn't deliver any convertible nutrients so the brain sends out a hunger message to compel the person to acquire calories from elsewhere – hence the desire to eat. Research in 2010 (Yang) concluded that replacing sugar with artificial sweeteners isn't the answer but that 'unsweetening the world's diet may be the key to reversing the obesity epidemic'.

The thirst-quenching properties of all soda drinks require a closer look too. As well as aspartame, a high number of sodas also include caffeine, which is a diuretic as well as a direct brain stimulant. This means soda drinks with caffeine are physiologically a dehydrating agent. This is one of the reasons why so many cans are consumed every day, and the thirst is never quenched. The liquid doesn't stay in the body long enough for adequate hydration. The very act of drinking so many cans or bottles of soda lulls people into thinking the messages their body is sending them can't possibly be about thirst, so they get confused, believe they must be hungry and then eat more instead.

Dr F Batmanghelidj, in his bestselling book *Your Body's Many Cries for Water*, is convinced that the long-term use of sodas in general, and diet sodas in particular, should be assumed to be responsible for some of the more serious health problems of our modern society.

Sports drinks seem to be popular with all sorts of people – even those who do not take part in any sports. They are formulated to replace the electrolytes lost through physical exertion but often contain artificial colouring and a host of unpronounceable chemical ingredients. This is one group of foods that would never pass the grandmother test, so are best avoided. If you're exhausted after a workout then plenty of water with a pinch of sea salt and half a banana should do the trick. Also, coconut water is now widely available in cartons or cans and is a natural isotonic drink that can provide many of the benefits promised by the manufacturers of sports drinks but without the science fiction. Still be watchful, though, as much of the coconut water that is sold varies in quality, with some having added sugar and preservatives and all sorts of unnecessary extras.

Sugars

Sugar comes disguised under about 50 different names and the food scientists are adding more all the time. If you are eating something with a label on it, then you are going to need to read it closely.

If you take sugar in your hot drinks, now would be a great opportunity to retrain your palette. It won't take very long for you really to relish your drinks without the added sweetness. To aid the transition, consider adding a slice of lemon to your cup of tea or consider upgrading your regular brand of tea to a select, single-estate brew. Using sugar is often a way of masking poor water quality too. Use a water filter jug to improve the quality of your tap water.

Sugar has a truly negative effect on your general health, weight loss potential and many specific health conditions. Ultimately, we recommend that added sugar stays permanently excluded from your food choices.

Dr Aseem Malhotra, a leading cardiologist based in London, is the science director of Action on Sugar. He has been instrumental in leading the debate about the public health implications of excess sugar consumption. He advocates that there is overwhelming scientific evidence that not only is added sugar an unnecessary source of additional calories but there is emerging evidence that the effects of excess sugar are harmful independent of body weight. He referred to a recent study published in the *Journal of the American Medical Association (JAMA)*. It revealed that adults in the USA who consume more than 25 per cent of their calories from added sugar trebled their risk of cardiovascular disease. This was compared with those who consumed less than 10 per cent from added sugar, even among the non-obese (Yang et al, 2014).

We live in the age of sugar, with a myriad of sugar derivatives and substitutes found everywhere in modern processed foods. When you start reading food labels you realise that sugars, hidden in plain sight, can be found almost everywhere, often in the least expected foods, from bread to soups to sauces. The only foolproof way of avoiding them is to diligently read labels and be vigilant with regard to what you choose to buy. It is an important health and weight loss consideration to reduce the amount of sugar consumed. It slips in under the radar in so many processed foods, of which one of the worst offenders is sweet drinks like root beer, ginger ale and cola. A typical 340 ml/12 fl oz serving contains 10 teaspoons of sugar and a typical teenager often drinks two cans a day. The average American eats almost 23 teaspoons of sugar each day, half of which is stirred into tea and coffee or baked into cakes and cookies.

Consider your own dependency on sweet things in your daily food choices. We are born with a natural attraction to sweetness. Breast milk, a human's first sustenance, has a sweet taste to make it irresistible to a newborn baby, and for many people their love affair with all things sweet continues throughout their lives without censure. Eating sugar stimulates the same pleasure centres in the brain that respond to the class A drugs heroin and cocaine. All appetising foods cause a similar response to varying degrees, but nowhere near as pronounced an effect as a hit of sugar.

The way the human brain responds to sweetness goes back almost to the beginning of humanity itself – some 20-odd million years ago when a craving for the sweetness of fruit in the autumn was a prerequisite for survival during the harsh, lean winters. Around this time, some of our ancestors developed an ability to take the fructose from the autumn fruit abundance and, due to a genetic mutation, became efficient at storing even small amounts of fructose (fruit sugar) as fat. Imagine how that genetic advantage was key to survival when winter arrived and all food sources were hard to come by. Now, take that premise forward to today; that same genetic advantage for metabolising fructose and storing it as fat is still prevalent in an era when we are literally awash with food.

It does not help that sugar masquerades under many different names. You can only be on the lookout for it if you know what to look for.

Sugar by any other name is still sugar

Peruse the list below and consider the many alternatives on offer to the white granulated table sugar you currently consume. We challenge you to find a substitute which provides more nutrients than the harm consuming sugar causes. There isn't one.

Agave, aka 'agave nectar', is marketed and sold as a healthy alternative to sugar but in reality is composed of 80 per cent fructose which is more than is found in HFCS (see later in the list, page 98). Stocked in health food stores with its relatively high price tag, you can be fooled into thinking you are making a wise choice when in reality it's just another laboratory-produced syrup almost entirely free of nutrients.

Barley malt syrup is a natural sweetener produced by cooking sprouted barley malt. It is dark brown in colour, with a pleasant malty taste. It is about half as sweet as honey. It is a natural product that contains some minerals and vitamins.

Beet sugar – About 30 per cent of the world's white sugar is made from processing this common agricultural crop into sugar. The advantage it has over cane sugar is that it can be grown in temperate climates in poor soil conditions and doesn't need the tropical conditions of cane sugar. After processing, the sugar from beets is white. If a producer wants to make brown sugar it has to be dyed with molasses from cane sugar. This conversion from white to brown isn't 100 per cent reliable as the molasses doesn't fully penetrate each grain of sugar, leaving an uneven distribution of flavour. For this reason it is avoided by home bakers and cake makers who favour the more reliable and expensive cane sugar.

Blackstrap molasses is produced as a by-product of manufacturing sugar from sugar cane. A stage in the processing creates molasses and if this syrup is then boiled a dark viscous liquid emerges known to Americans as blackstrap. It is often promoted as a healthier alternative to standard sugar; however, avoid sulphured varieties and opt for unsulphured as these are higher in antioxidants and trace minerals. Two table spoons of blackstrap contain 13.2 per cent of the recommended daily intake (RDI) of iron, 11.7 per cent RDI calcium and 7.3 per cent RDI magnesium.

Brown rice syrup, aka 'rice syrup' or 'rice malt': even though it is made from brown rice, this syrup is still a refined sugar. It is actually higher in calories than ordinary sugar, varying (depending on the brand) between 55 and 75 calories per tablespoon compared to 48 calories in table sugar.

Brown sugar: there are no discernible health benefits to swapping from white sugar to brown sugar and although it contains some trace minerals they are present in only tiny amounts.

Buttered sugar, aka 'butter cream' or 'butter fondant' is a well-beaten mixture of icing sugar and butter for use in cake making for fillings, toppings or piped as decoration. It can be home-made (a ratio of 2:1 sugar to butter) or commercially bought and may include additional artificial colours and flavourings.

Cane juice (or cane juice crystals) is often sold as a healthy alternative to white sugar but is in effect the same as eating standard sugar in syrup form.

Cane juice (evaporated) is derived from sugar cane syrup to make a highly concentrated sweetener. Also know as 'panela' or 'raspadura', the Latin American version is basically just pure sugar.

Cane sugar Is a slightly less processed version of white sugar. It retains a colour closer to that of its natural state but should still be treated with caution and does not impart any additional health benefits.

Caramel aka 'toffee', aka 'butterscotch', are all types of confectioners' products made by mixing varying quantities of sugar, cream and butter. Different cooking temperatures change the consistency from soft and chewy to crunchy.

Carob syrup is made from carob seeds and pulp. It is mildly sweet and is used in baking as a substitute for chocolate.

Caster sugar is simply more finely ground than standard white granulated sugar. (Its name comes from the Victorian era 'sugar caster' that was used to sprinkle sugar on food.) It can come from sugar cane or from sugar beet and consists purely of sucrose (see below).

Coconut sugar is often promoted as a healthier alternative to table sugar as it does contain some trace elements and nutrients but it has none of the healthy aspects of coconut oil, milk or water.

Confectioner's sugar aka 'Icing sugar' is powdered sugar made from white cane sugar used to top cakes with icing and frosting preparation as well as a wide range of baked goods; it has a high calorie count and is quickly absorbed into the bloodstream, causing spikes in blood sugar levels.

Corn syrup, corn syrup solids and corn sweetener are commonly used as sweeteners in processed foods and powdered beverage mixes; a large and growing proportion of corn grown in the US, and now the world over, is genetically modified. Genetic modification is generally associated with intensive use of herbicides and pesticides. Corn syrup is much higher in fructose (see below) than table sugar.

Crystalline fructose is made from corn. It is increasingly commonly found in baked goods and ice cream. It is chemically different from its popular predecessor, high fructose corn syrup (HFCS) which consumers are increasingly avoiding. However, crystalline fructose physiologically has the same effects and can be the cause of gastrointestinal upset and aggravate symptoms in individuals with irritable bowel syndrome (IBS).

Date sugar, as the name suggests, is made from macerated dates and is a less processed form of sugar. It' uses are limited as it does not dissolve in water but has its uses in breads and baking.

Demerara sugar (and golden sugar, which is a more finely ground version) may have more nutrients than standard white sugar but be aware that any nutritional advantage is barely significant.

Dextran is a highly processed sugar often used as a food additive.

Dextrose is a simple sugar chemically identical to glucose, the sugar found in the bloodstream. As well as a common sweetener in a wide range of products, it has medical applications when dissolved in a solution and administered intravenously. The body is able to metabolise dextrose quickly as a source of energy.

Diastatic malt, produced from barley, is many times sweeter than standard sugar. It is associated with the salivary enzyme diastase which helps with the breakdown of sugars for absorption and can contribute to blood sugar spikes.

Erythritol is a sugar found naturally in pears, watermelon and grapes. It is used as a sweetener in chewing gum, some baked goods and drinks.

Ethyl malto's scientific sounding name should be warning enough that this laboratory-manufactured compound used in baked goods is completely artificial and has an unnaturally high sugar content.

Fructose occurs naturally in fruits and honey, which in our recent past would only have been available, and consumed, seasonally and sparingly. Now fructose is found in baked goods and sodas. It is one of the key sugars that has been indicated to be a major contributor to rising obesity and diabetes rates over the past several decades. As well as their modern-day role as an additive, fruits themselves have also been selectively bred to increase their sweetness by increasing the level of fructose they contain. Selectively bred apples and grapes, for instance, are almost unrecognisable from their original, natural varieties. Some varieties of small apple sold specifically as a healthy addition to children's lunch boxes are often the worse culprits.

Fruit juice concentrates are made by removing water from fruit juice. The process also removes the scant nutrients which would be present in freshly squeezed juice. However, all fruit juices, freshly squeezed or concentrated, are an unnatural way to consume the nutrients from fruit. Fruit is best consumed as whole fruits, in small quantities, and where possible it is best to choose traditional varieties of fruit that celebrate their natural sharp taste. Tropical fruits that have been picked unripe and then ripened artificially are particularly high in fructose.

Galactose is a derivative of the sugar in milk – lactose. It is found in processed foods and fast foods. Even though it is a naturally occurring sugar, it has been observed to increase blood pressure, and is a contributing factor to diabetes. As a milk derivative it may cause problems for people with a dairy intolerance. Glucose, like fructose, is found in sugar cane, fruits, honey and latterly in baked goods. It is also the simplest building block of carbohydrates so all carbohydrates consumed break down to become glucose for absorption, fuel and storage. Consumption of glucose has been linked to some heart diseases and the prevalence of obesity. Just as with fructose, this is a natural sugar. It is just not natural that it is consumed in such quantities.

Golden syrup is made from corn syrup. Drizzled over pancakes and desserts, it is comprised of three sugars – fructose, glucose and sucrose, which itself is broken down to become glucose in the human body.

HFCS or 'high-fructose corn syrup' is cheaper than sugar to manufacture and has replaced traditional corn sugar in a wide variety of products from jams to sauces, to soda pops, as well as fast foods, cereals and breads. When you read HFCS on a product label, think twice and don't buy it. The cheapness of HFCS has led to an increase in the availability of super-sized soda drinks with little or no additional cost to the manufacturer but delivering larger than ever portion sizes laden with obesity-inducing quantities of sweetness. It is a controversial addition to the 'frankenfood' sugar arsenal, with large amounts of money spent by its advocates to prove it has no medical ill effects on the consumer. In paleo terms it is to be avoided as one of the types of ingredient that did not exist 50 years ago. It is yet another modern additive invented by men and women working in laboratories to take advantage of US government-subsidised cheap corn crops. Remember from the fructose listing here that humans are genetically predisposed to efficiently store fructose as fat and that HFCS is no different, in encouraging body fat storage.

Honey contains so much sugar it is practically off the charts! Stirring it into a hot drink almost certainly kills any potential health benefits, assuming they haven't already been reduced or obliterated by the process of pasteurisation. Raw honey has antiviral, antibacterial and antifungal properties and might be better used by being applied topically to cuts and abrasions instead of eaten.

Inverted sugar, aka 'invert sugar', is a corn sugar modified using an animal enzyme, making it *verboten* to vegans, vegetarians, observant Jews and Muslims. It is a commonly used sugar in a wide range of baked goods, sodas and general confectionery.

Jaggery is the name for the traditional process originating in Asia and Africa of creating unprocessed sugar concentrate from dates, cane juice or palm sap without separating out the molasses or crystals. The resultant product (also called 'jaggery') is semi-solid, softer than sugar and amorphous. It varies in colour from yellow to golden brown to dark brown. It is more complex than sugar with longer chains of sucrose and therefore releases its energy more slowly than processed sugar. The centuries-old process is the antithesis of the highly mechanised sugar industry and most jaggery comes from remote rural places, arriving at local markets and rarely exported out of its country of origin, although some specialist Asian or African food shops stock it.

Lactose is the natural sugar found in cows' milk. A high proportion of the adult population of the world is lactose intolerant, so even if you are comfortable drinking milk produced by cows to feed their calves, it might be the cause of bloating, cramps and digestive disorders, and of problems with mucus in the sinuses, ears and chest. Exclude all dairy products, including cheese, for a period of a few weeks to see if this improves symptoms.

Luo han guo, aka 'monk fruit' (translation), is obtained from a plant native to the Guangxi province in southwestern China. Although known in China for almost a thousand years, it has only recently been introduced to the West. It is a natural zero-calorie sweetener some

300 times sweeter than sugar. It also scores zero on the glycaemic index (the index of the impact of different sugars and carbohydrates on blood sugar levels) and is purported to be suitable for diabetics. BioVittoria company in New Zealand has begun to cultivate the monk fruit and grow it commercially for export.

Malt syrup results from a three-stage process beginning with germinated grain that has been fermented. Although any grain would work, the chosen grain is usually barley. It is used in baked goods and some diabetic prepared foods. It is half as sweet as table sugar and has a distinctively malty flavour.

Maltodextrin is another highly processed common food additive derived from corn and is found in beer, sweets and a whole raft of prepared foods. It has been found to be a trigger for those suffering from coeliac disease and other wheat and corn allergies.

Maltose, aka 'malt sugar', is a component of malt and it is the sugar that is a natural element of beer. It is made up of two glucose molecules and is known to be a significant cause of weight gain.

Maple syrup might allay some of your health concerns when drizzling it onto pancakes and waffles instead of golden syrup, but even the finest, most expensive brand you can buy has little nutritional value. It is primarily a sucrose with some glucose and fructose.

Molasses are derived from boiling down either sugar cane or sugar beet and are at least a good source of iron and calcium but have been known to trigger allergies, and even asthma attacks, due to the high sulphur content.

Muscovado sugar is the big brother of brown sugar (sucrose) and are that little bit less processed, although without any significant nutritional value.

Organic oat syrup, aka 'avena sativa', is a common ingredient in breakfast muesli bars, baked goods and even ice cream. It has been claimed to be a rich source of antioxidants but is still highly calorific.

Organic white sugar flatters to deceive as it is basically standard white sugar, as processed and refined as any other.

Panocha, aka 'brown sugar fudge', is made from a health-defeating combination of brown sugar, butter and milk.

Rice bran syrup, aka 'rice malt syrup', aka 'rice syrup', is made from fermenting brown rice. The resultant brown sludge is over half made up of the sugar maltotriose, followed by 45 per cent maltose and 3 per cent and glucose. By the time this sweetener gets broken down in the gut it is basically just 100 per cent glucose, the same as processed white sugar.

Sorghum, aka 'sorghum syrup', contains high levels of dietary fibre and is used in beer, cereals, baked goods and alcoholic beverages. It is pretty much devoid of nutrients and there are other less calorifically loaded ways of obtaining fibre.

Stevia is a sweetener derived from the leaves of a shrub native to tropical and subtropical America. It is growing in popularity as a calorie-free alternative to sugar. It is available in granular or syrup form.

Sucrose, aka 'table sugar', is often at the forefront of any debate concerning the increasing incidence of obesity, diabetes and heart disease. It is what is called a 'di-saccharide', being made of two glucose molecules; the body needs to break it down to glucose before it can be absorbed so it does not produce quite such an instant 'hit' as glucose itself.

Sugar, or 'table sugar' to distinguish it from the broader meaning 'sugar', is the household name we give to sucrose, which is derived from either sugar cane or sugar beet. In many ways it is more benign than HFCS (see above), its cheaper replacement. Don't let that fool you though. Long gone are the days when sugar was considered as rare a commodity as saffron. It is everywhere. Kidney and renal specialist, Richard Johnson at the University of Colorado Denver, in an interview with Rich Cohen for *National Geographic Magazine* (Cohen, 2013) said, 'It seems like every time I study an illness, and trace a path to the first cause, I find my way back to sugar.' He continued, 'Why is it that one-third of adults (worldwide) have high blood pressure, when in 1900 only five per cent had high blood pressure? And, why did 153 million people have diabetes in 1980, and now we're up to 347 million? And, why are more and more Americans obese?'

Answering his own rhetorical questions he said, 'Sugar, we believe, is one of the culprits, if not the major culprit.'

'Syrup' as a descriptive term features in many of the names of sugar derivatives. In fact, anything called syrup should come with a health warning as although some are more benign – being less refined – than others, all of them are high in calories and practically devoid of any nutritional benefits.

Tapioca syrup is often interchanged with maple syrup. However, just as with maple syrup, it doesn't have nutritional advantage over any other basic sugar syrup.

Treacle is made from the refining of sugar cane or sugar beet and is the starting ingredient of a whole raft of syrups of varying descriptions. It comprises the sugar trio of sucrose (which is made up of glucose), fructose and glucose. It contains no other nutrients.

Turbinado, aka 'raw sugar', is just sugar by another name, and is metabolised by the body in exactly the same way as any other sugar.

Xylitol is widely used in sugar-free chewing gum and sweets. It is naturally found in low concentrations in the fibrous parts of many fruits and vegetables. Highly mechanised extraction processes can also extract this sweetener from hardwoods or the outer fibrous cover of corncobs. It has a medical application to reduce ear infections. (It is worth noting that even when the small amount in sweets or candy is eaten it is poisonous to dogs and should a dog eat any product containing xylitol it should be taken to a veterinary clinic immediately.)

Note: When reading food lables, be aware that any ingredient ending in 'ose' is a sugar.

Vegetable oils

Vegetable oils only became popular during the last few decades as saturated fats became demonised as a direct cause of heart disease and raised cholesterol levels. The chief oils in question are canola oil/rapeseed oil, soybean oil, sunflower oil, corn oil, cottonseed oil and safflower oil. Just because they have the word 'vegetable' in their name doesn't mean they are necessarily healthy. The extraction of oil from seeds has only been possible for around a hundred years and it is a complex and unappetising process which produces an oil that is high in omega-6 fatty acids but without the omega-3 fatty acids we need to balance them up. (Both omega-6 and omega-3 are *essential* fatty acids for us humans, but current research indicates that the ratio should be somewhere between 3:1 and 1:1. This is because omega-6 promotes inflammation – needed to deal with injury and infection – and omega-3 reduces inflammation. Our modern Western diet is pro-inflammatory because the ratio is nearing 18:1 – see page 46).

Promoted as a healthy alternative to saturated fats, as well as supermarkets selling these oils for home use, they are used in the manufacture of thousands of commercially produced foods. This is a particularly important example of misinformation from the food giants and a reminder of the need to read every product's label closely.

Meal choices that work hard for you

The following are popular meal choices taken from the food diaries of some of the clients we have worked with. You can see they are often simple meals focusing on a protein food with vegetables or salad. Remember you can make positive changes to your eating habits incrementally, one meal at a time.

Breakfast ideas

Bacon, two eggs cooked any way, cherry tomatoes

Grilled sausages (only best quality with little or no rusk) and cherry tomatoes

Chicken leg and mixed vegetables (or veg leftovers, if you have them)

Venison sausages (grilled), lettuce and tomatoes

Cheese and ham omelette

Herb omelette

Selection of cold meats and goats' cheese

Smoked haddock or salmon

Mushrooms fried in butter or ghee

Kippers or any smoked fish available.

Lunch ideas

Smoked salmon and green salad

Best quality sausages and green salad

Beef burger (no bun) with green salad

Two chicken legs and green salad

Ham and goats' cheese salad

Chicken breast with peas and broccoli

Tuna steak and homemade mayo

Lettuce or spinach with chicken and red peppers

Sardines and green salad

Cream of cauliflower soup

Broccoli soup.

An ideal lunch is a generous serving of mixed green salad made of celery, red onion or spring onions, round or cos lettuce (avoid iceberg lettuce if possible) or spinach or rocket leaves and avocado with sardines, sliced cold meats or chicken. Serve with a dressing based on a cold-pressed oil of your choice. Make sure there are plenty of green vegetables and the portion sustains you, ideally through to the next mealtime so you don't feel the need to snack.

Dinner ideas

Minced beef casserole

Homemade cream of chicken soup

Pork chop and mixed vegetables

Mackerel or any other tasty fish with green salad or selection of greens as detailed above

Steamed fish with green salad or greens as above

Shredded duck and vegetables

Meatballs with melted cheese and courgette-spaghetti (see Swapping old for new on page xx.)

Homemade shepherd's pie with celeriac topping

White fish in garlic sauce

White fish with herb crust and salad

Chicken curry with cauliflower rice and green salad (see Swapping old for new on page xx.)

Steak and green salad with sweet potato hand-cut chips

Chicken with honey and mustard rub and green salad

Lamb shish kebabs with Greek-style feta cheese salad

Beef bourguignon

Lamb chops with stir-fry vegetables

Chicken or beef stir-fry

Beef casserole

Fish – preferably oily, such as mackerel, salmon or sea bass

Grilled steak, chicken or fish with green salad or cooked greens.

Dessert ideas

Fruit berry medley with full fat Greek yoghurt or cream, or coconut yoghurt if avoiding dairy

Raspberries or other berries (fresh or frozen) and cream or coconut yoghurt of cream

Chocolate mousse made from 70 per cent + dark chocolate and eggs (one egg to 50 g chocolate)

Sprinkle desserts with ground almonds or ground pumpkin seeds.

Snack foods that are good to go

Protein and healthy fat-based meals give you high levels of satiety and should keep you feeling fuller for longer, until your next meal. If you do feel peckish between meals, then keep your choices to the proportions in the food pyramid on page 111.

Remember, though, the aim is to have just three meals a day, not the constant grazing that is common with higher carbohydrate eating plans. If you feel you need to snack every mid-morning and mid-afternoon and are still looking for food after your main evening meal is over, then you may need to reassess portion size and the protein and fat levels in your meals. Cravings for sweet snacks can be a sign of poor blood sugar control.

Here are some sustaining alternatives:

Celery with a small piece of mature cheddar cheese

Celery with pâté

Apple or pear with a small piece of Roquefort (blue vein) cheese

Apple or pear and a handful of toasted salt-free nuts and seeds

Peppermint tea, green tea or fruit teas

Handful of salt-free nuts and seeds

Small handful of walnuts and a pear

Small handful of almonds and Brazil nuts with a pear

Handful of macadamia nuts.

Putting it all together

Be present

At every meal, eat away from electronic distractions of all kinds. If you want to listen to the radio while you eat, then ensure you turn off the news station and switch to soothing music. Allowing yourself to be calm while you eat enables your body to access the available nutrition in your food better.

Sur la table

Adopt the French tradition of sitting at a table to eat. Ideally leave your desk or sofa and serve the food you intend to eat on a plate in front of you. If you're away from home for lunch, invest in a couple of well-designed food containers. A park bench is not a table but is still infinitely preferable to eat lunch from a plastic box on your lap to eating distractedly at your desk while checking your emails. Even if it is just for 20 minutes, break up your day and go outside whenever possible.

Make it awesome

Look at your food. Is this meal an expression of your own high self-regard? Does it appeal to your appetite and your senses? Is there ample protein there? Chicken or tinned sardines, sliced beef, hard-boiled eggs or a flavoursome full-fat cheese. Does your meal look colourful and varied? Does it have a salad component or raw grated vegetables dressed with olive oil and lemon juice? Does the meal include a complex carbohydrate such as brown rice or a sweet potato?

If this meal is not an ideal expression of how you want to care for yourself nutritionally, then what can you improve or change to make it awesome next time?

Snack stash

Have a stash of healthy snack foods so that, should you become hungry between meals, you can satisfy your hunger with a healthy choice. For instance, you could have a tart apple with a small bag of unsalted walnuts, or a small box of chopped vegetable crudités with a pesto or humus dip.

Hydrate yourself

Throughout the day, drink plenty of fresh water. If you are drinking coffee aim to have one cup in the morning to drink black with a teaspoon of coconut oil stirred in. Augment drinking water with green tea or unsweetened natural fruit teas, to add variety.

Meal planning and preparation

Before shopping, plan your meals for the week and make a shopping list based on this. Planning is everything and will contribute hugely to your success. It may well feel effortful to begin with as thinking ahead is the complete opposite to the mindless choices of old. As the changes you make become second nature and you begin to reap the rewards from your new habits, this will soon become the new normal for you.

Remember:
- the greater the variety of foods equals the greater the variety of nutrients
- eat vegetables of as many colours as possible every day
- eat at least one serving of raw vegetables every day.

Be strategic

Keep it simple:
- Decide on a soup, a slow-cooked casserole and a basic salad or two for the week ahead.
- Batch cook at the weekend with the idea of freezing meal-size portions for mid-week lunches.

- While cooking on a Sunday, double up by roasting extra vegetables that can be eaten with salads or served with cold meats later.

The weekend is an ideal time for making a batch of egg-based breakfast muffins (see page 47) to take to work or a large pot of bone broth to freeze for future soups.

Get inspired

Do your research online, or in long-ignored cookery books you may already have, to inspire you to add variety to your meals. Remember to look outside your own culture for inspiration, especially for delicious vegetable-based meals from India, the Middle East and the Far East to incorporate and inform your own cooking.

Source the best

Break the strangle-hold the supermarkets have on our food choices by shopping in a different way. The easiest way to find local produce and discover what vegetables are in season is to visit local farmers' markets; there you can buy natural-looking fresh fruit and discover independent cheese and yoghurt producers alongside artisan bakeries. Browsing the stalls is an enjoyable way to spend an hour over a weekend even if it is only once a month. Make it social by inviting a friend or your partner to come along and make some discoveries with you.

If it's not possible to visit a farmers' market for produce, consider signing up to a box scheme delivered to your door or use the internet to source money-saving deals on pasture-fed meat or specialist fish suppliers.

Read every label

Let go of what you know and check every ingredient. If a food comes with a label on it, treat it with extreme caution and read it thoroughly. Do you want those ingredients with unpronounceable scientific names in your body? Hopefully not.

The enduring meaning of breaking bread

Much disordered eating happens in isolation from oneself and disassociation from supportive and loving friends. If you recognise that you have isolated yourself and withdrawn from possible sources of love and support, we urge you to make changes. Where possible, we recommend you eat at least some of your meals in a social setting, either at home or in a café or restaurant with friends and loved ones.

Share the food you have prepared as a gesture of love to yourself and with those others who count in your life.

Strive for progress, not perfection

Foods you need to incorporate into your daily diet are shown opposite in our healthy-eating pyramid. It gives you an idea of the ratios to aim for. Think of these basic ratios when you plan an individual meal or when you look ahead for several days of meals.

It really helps, especially while you are learning these new eating principles, to keep a food and mood diary so that you can track the food combinations that work for you, bearing in mind your levels of satiety versus hunger and perceived energy levels (page 127).

As you experience for yourself the numerous health benefits of following these guidelines the more you will want to apply these ratios to as many meals as you can.

Health benefits

Do not take 'healthy eating' on trust. An exploration of how to improve your nutrition and optimise your health asks you to take responsibility for yourself. It asks that you no longer blindly choose pre-packaged meals or snacks stamped with the words 'Healthy Choice' or 'Nature's Finest', 'Natural', or 'Original'. These are simply marketing terms made up by the advertising industry to lull you into a false sense of security that you are making healthy food choices. It is the same with the use of illustrations of pastoral scenes on pre-packaged meat, dairy and eggs. Those idyllic images or advertising text that promises 'farm assured' or 'locally sourced' or 'farm fresh' are cynically chosen to imply high welfare for livestock whether that is the reality or not.

We ask that you take nothing for granted and read the small print on packaged meat, diary, eggs and cheese and get to know the meaning of the different quality of farm or welfare assurance logos printed on labels. That way you can make informed choices for yourself. Alternatively, ask your butcher or store owner about the provenance of the produce they sell. The more questions we ask the more we reinforce that we care about animal welfare and that it influences our buying decisions.

Compassion in World Farming (CIWF) established the following five key welfare issues for farmed animals under the heading of 'The Five Freedoms'. They are:
1. Freedom from hunger and thirst by ready access to fresh water and a diet to maintain full health and vigour.
2. Freedom from discomfort by providing an appropriate environment, including shelter and a comfortable resting area.
3. Freedom from pain, injury or disease by prevention or rapid diagnosis and treatment.
4. Freedom to express normal behaviour by providing sufficient space, proper facilities and company of the animal's own kind.
5. Freedom from fear and distress by ensuring conditions and treatment which avoid mental suffering.

CIWF (2012) reviewed how the numerous welfare schemes run by organisations such as the Soil Association, Royal Society for the Protection of Animals (RSPA) and commercial organisations measure up to their benchmark. For instance, the Soil Association's Gold accreditation in the UK for pig husbandry is equivalent to a Silver when compared with the more rigorous parameters of CIWF's Five Freedoms. The Red Tractor scheme is a popular welfare scheme commonly seen on the packaging of meat in the UK's supermarkets. It certifies the food was produced to certain quality standards, but for some farm animals that unfortunately does not adequately reach the standards required for even CIWF's most lenient Bronze award.

As you move your food choices away from processed and packaged foods and make informed choice about the quality of food you buy, including the welfare and origin of farmed animal produce, you will be taking steps towards long-lasting improvements in your health. This is true not just for your digestive system, but you will also be doing the very best you can for yourself both physically and emotionally because what you eat affects both your body and your mind.

Boost your immune system

Altogether, around 70 per cent of the immune system is located in the gut. It is therefore vital to maximise the health of your gut and its population of helpful microbes (see page 16) to support your immune system. It is beneficial to eat foods regularly that do not trigger your immune system to react and have minimal chances of causing allergic reactions. Current thinking is that eating potentially allergenic foods that do not cause a reaction is important in staving off the development of allergies in the future. For instance, someone who suffers from a peanut allergy might be advised to eat all other nuts regularly so they do not go on to develop other nut allergies. For someone suffering serious allergic reactions this approach requires the professional guidance of your medical practitioner and testing for possible allergies only under medical supervision.

The term 'clean foods' or 'eating clean' gets bandied about by celebrity cooks and the like but the truth is there are no clean foods or dirty foods. There are, however, foods that support your immune system and those that do not.

A low-carbohydrate, real food approach to eating is ideal in many ways as it favours eating from a wide range of natural foods, including proteins, vegetables and healthy fats. Replacing simple carbohydrates with complex carbohydrates is the perfect way to manage blood sugar levels. 'Simple carbohydrates' would be sugars of all types (see page 94) and 'refined carbs', such as white bread, pasta and white rice, all of which are digested and absorbed very quickly to produce a stressful blood sugar spike. It is recognised that poor blood sugar control leads to insulin resistance – a declining response to the insulin the body produces to manage sugar levels. Dietary sugar also discourages good bacteria in the gut and stimulates the growth of bacteria that ferment sugars, leading to bloating. There are food recommendations in foods to marry on page 69 and how to swap your usual carbs for healthier alternatives in Swapping old for new on page 56.

Eat your way out of depression

Nutrition-related health issues seem to take an age to become part of accepted medical practice. The medical establishment requires comprehensive scientific evaluation, randomised trials and peer review before a new drug can be licensed, for instance. The pharmaceutical company has to weigh up the costs of research and development versus the potential profit to be made from launching a successful product that can earn a good return on their investment. (When you add in the factor that 80 per cent of their budget goes on marketing, it is clear the stakes are high indeed.) As real food is simply real food and can't be licensed, branded or patented, there is little impetus for the medical community to fund costly research.

Medical research over the last couple of decades has, nevertheless, highlighted how an unhealthy gut can contribute to many physical diseases and these findings are becoming more accepted in mainstream medicine. Clinicians increasingly agree that the gut-brain axis also plays a crucial part in emotional wellbeing, including the development of conditions as diverse as chronic fatigue syndrome, depression and autism.

The gut-brain axis is a way of describing the interrelationship between gut health and brain health. The various aspects of digestion are controlled via the vagus nerves by a complex set of neurons embedded in the oesophagus, stomach, intestines, colon and rectum. The brain sends messages to all the nerves in your body, including the neurons that control digestion. All work efficiently enough until a person is anxious or stressed on an ongoing basis. You perhaps know for yourself that if you are feeling nervous your stomach can feel upset and queasy. The reason for this is that strong negative emotions, stress and anxiety increase cortisol and adrenaline, which then stimulate the sympathetic nervous system and shut down the parasympathetic nervous system, which includes control of the gut. This causes a physical chain reaction:

Reduction in pancreatic enzyme production

Reduction in gall bladder function

Reduction in the production of stomach acid

Slowing down of peristalsis – the involuntary muscle movements essential for moving food efficiently through the intestines for the absorption of nutrients

Reduction in blood flow to the intestines

Suppression of the intestinal immune system.

In the short term, this allows the body to focus its resources on 'fight or flight' – a good survival mechanism. However, with ongoing stress and anxiety, this cumulative slowing down and suppression of the digestive process can, over a prolonged period, lead to a condition called 'small intestinal bacterial overgrowth' (SIBO). As the digestive process is compromised by stress and anxiety, the lack of stomach acid allows the stomach and small intestine – which should both be pretty much microbe-free – to be colonised by unhealthy bacteria, and yeasts, causing foods to be fermented rather than digested. In addition to gas and bloating, compromised digestion leads to declining absorption of nutrients, which contributes to the loss of the co-factors needed for good digestion, and consequently further gut problems.

Now consider this situation lasting for extended periods of time. The integrity of the gut lining may be compromised, contributing to gut permeability ('leaky gut') that may be sufficient to produce chronic low-grade inflammation.

The inflammatory process includes the production of cytokines, chemical signals of inflammation that are carried by the blood to the brain. The cytokines can activate cells in the brain called 'microglia' – the brain's immune cells – so that the inflammation originating in the gut thereby causes widespread inflammation in the rest of the body, including in the brain.

The impact of brain inflammation is that the brain has reduced nerve conductance which – guess what – shows up as depression, anxiety and stress.

This vicious circle can self-perpetuate and requires long-term changes to heal the gut, which in turn will help to heal the brain. This is done through changes in behaviour and improving levels of nutrition through changes to food choices. To improve your natural resilience to stress it is important to increase the amount of healthy polyunsaturated omega-3 oils in your diet, so look for oily fish, grass-fed meats and butter made from the millk of grass-fed dairy herds. Good plant sources include hemp seeds, linseeds, chia and some nuts and nut oils (macadamia, almond) – see page 46.

If you consider yourself to be depressed it will be helpful for your recovery to manage your stress levels, improve your sleep patterns (see page 18) and add nutritious and gut-healing foods into your regular eating plan (see Foods to embrace and enjoy page 69).

Do bear in mind, however, that you may also need professional help if you have been suffering from this debilitating psychological disorder for some time. Please make sure you are accessing all the medical and psychological support you need. Try hard not to add isolation to an already challenging situation.

Gut health

As we have said, the health of your digestive system is increasingly acknowledged to be the key to your potential to be physically healthy and well. You cannot be fully well if your digestion is out of kilter. However, you may not be aware that your digestive functioning is impaired. There are many factors that affect your digestion that are commonplace in our busy, modern lives. They include poor quality sleep, stress and anxiety (as explained above), stimulants such as alcohol and recreational drugs, and many prescription medications, including antibiotics.

Feeling sluggish, bloated or out of sorts becomes the normal way of feeling if it goes on for long enough. Add in processed foods and fast foods that are calorifically dense and nutritionally poor, and your body becomes progressively less efficient at supporting a strong immune system and fighting infections. Perhaps you're already beginning to recognise yourself from this brief description. You do not need to have had a medical diagnosis of Crohn's disease (IBD) or irritable bowel syndrome (IBS) to be experiencing the symptoms of digestive disruption. How about occasional, mysterious abdominal pain or fluctuating between diarrhoea and constipation, or indigestion, heartburn and flatulence? Many people live with these symptoms for decades without ever consulting a doctor. It is as if they are resigned to feeling below par, and that this is what they should expect to feel like.

It's worth taking a moment or two to really understand how your digestion works, and what it needs to function optimally. So, simply put, digestion is the process of turning all the food you eat into fuel in a form that your body can use.

The process of digestion subtly begins when you see and smell the food you are going to eat. The peeling, chopping and preparing of your meal helps trigger neurological messages to be sent to your digestive system to prepare your body to receive nutrition. This is why the practice of mindfulness is so valuable when eating to improve digestion. It is also a powerful counterpoint to the habit of eating while distracted at your desk, or while driving, or in a zoned out state when you are barely aware of what you are consuming at all.

When you eat, the food you chew and swallow mixes with digestive enzymes produced from cells lining the inner surface of your mouth. These start to break starches down to sugar. The food then passes into your stomach, where specialised cells in its lining produce gastric acid and digestive enzymes that break down proteins. In addition to the enzymes produced by your body, additional useful enzymes are contained in raw, fresh foods. The enzymes found in food are particularly susceptible to destruction by heat and processing so are most prevalent in raw, salad-type foods. If your usual food choices are mainly cooked, or heavily processed, then these enzymes will not be present to aid digestion. This puts additional stress on your digestive system, and the enzymes produced by your body have to work harder.

Enzymes in the stomach and small intestine are essential to the process of breaking down complex proteins, fats and carbohydrates in your food into smaller and simpler constituents. In addition, the correct amount of stomach acid is critical for breaking down proteins into the individual amino acids that our bodies need for just about every biological process.

The food progresses from your stomach to your small intestine. The digestive enzymes here continue the process of breaking it down until it is small enough to be absorbed into your bloodstream – or lymphatic system in the case of fats – allowing you to access and absorb the macro-nutrients, vitamins and minerals your body needs.

Such a complex system can meet with problems at any point. If you are not producing adequate stomach acid, or do not have enough digestive enzymes, then the macro and micro nutrients in your food will not be fully absorbed. Meanwhile, poorly digested foods will remain in your sluggish digestive system; this slow transit time further encourages the growth of harmful bacteria, fungi and yeasts in your small intestine and colon. This can lead to irritation to the lining of your gut, causing inflammation and leading to 'leaky gut', which is now thought by many outside the mainstream medical establishment to cause a wide range of health problems. 'Leaky gut syndrome' although recognised on the NHS website with a 'last reviewed' date of early 2015 (http://www.nhs.uk/conditions/leaky-gut-syndrome/Pages/Introduction.aspx) includes the proviso that there is currently little evidence that health conditions are in fact caused by having a 'leaky gut'. Gastroenterologist and Director of the Center for Human Nutrition at the Cleveland Clinic, Donald Kirby, MD, was quoted on the medical website WebMD (http://www.webmd.com/digestive-disorders/features/leaky-gut-syndrome) saying: 'From an MD's standpoint, it's a very gray area. Physicians don't know enough about the gut, which is our biggest immune system organ. Leaky gut syndrome isn't a diagnosis taught in medical school. Instead, leaky gut really means you've got a diagnosis that still needs to be made. ... You hope that your doctor is a good-enough Sherlock Holmes, but sometimes it is very hard to make a diagnosis.'

Lack of acid and enzymes in the stomach can also lead to heartburn and acid reflux as foods ferment and back up. In addition to chronic stress and anxiety, ageing is a primary consideration in declining stomach acid, as is adrenal fatigue and failure, usually caused by our ever-present foe – chronic stress.

Optimum levels of stomach acid and healthy digestive enzymes can be encouraged and we guide you towards the most beneficial food choices for this (see Fermented foods on page 72).

Hormones and you

Doctors see so many patients with symptoms so similar that they have often been known to use the abbreviation TATT to sum up in their notes when a patient explains how they feel 'tired all the time'.

It can just seem like an inevitable by-product of modern-day living, with many people working long days and going to bed later than they intended. Add into the mix a constant state of mental over-stimulation from using smart phones and laptops all the time and it is not surprising people complain of feeling burnt out and exhausted.

The hypothalamus is the part of the brain that regulates the body's response to stress and relays information to all the body's organs with the goal of maintaining balance – what is called 'homeostasis'. The body is helped to maintain homeostasis by the thyroid gland that acts like a finely tuned sensor responding to a range of stimuli, in response to which it will increase or decrease the body's metabolic rate. It may come as no surprise to read that both the hypothalamus and the thyroid gland can become over-stimulated by long-term stress so that the body remains in a heightened state of anxiety and the thyroid gland can eventually become over- or under-active, both of which states have serious repercussions on general health and wellbeing.

The medical profession will hear the symptoms of TATT along with other clues, such as struggling to lose weight, feeling cold and feeling exhausted upon waking, and from this – if blood tests confirm the diagnosis – prescribe synthetic thyroid hormones. This can be beneficial for some patients but it does nothing to correct the hormonal imbalance that has caused the thyroid gland to become over-worked and under-active in the first place.

Nutrition has an important part to play in helping the thyroid gland back into balance. Key to this is improving gut health (see page 116). Likewise, it is recognised that sugar has a detrimental effect on gut health and reducing or eliminating sugar from your diet can prove beneficial for an under-active thyroid.

Vegetarians can thrive too

If you follow a vegetarian diet then you are by definition particularly discerning about what you eat. Being a vegetarian, though, does not mean that you are necessarily immune to eating a diet that causes you to carry more weight than you may wish, or one that affects your digestive health.

Many vegetarians place a great deal of emphasis on carbohydrates in their diet, using bread, potatoes and pasta as the basis for both main meals and snacks. However, this can be easily adjusted to shift the balance to lower carbohydrates and higher healthy fats and oils, together with adequate amounts of protein, so that you can reap the benefits of being able to achieve successful weight loss while still eating from your chosen food range.

For instance, a low-carbohydrate emphasis for a vegetarian would be to encourage eating fresh, locally-sourced and organic (where possible) vegetables and fruits. Purists might not eat legumes because they contain phytic acid, but for vegetarians they are a useful source of protein and fibre. The main legumes are:

Alfalfa	Peanuts
Black-eyed pea	Peas
Broad beans/Fava beans	Petits pois
Cannellini beans	Pinto beans
Chickpeas	Red kidney beans
Green and yellow peas	Runner beans
Kidney beans	Snow peas
Lentils	Southern peas
Mexican black or red beans	Soybeans
Mung beans	Sugar snap peas

Phytic acid in legumes can cause digestive issues and inhibit the absorption of other nutrients. It can be reduced/eliminated by soaking the beans for a minimum of 18 hours before cooking. The same is true for nuts – soak them first overnight and then dry them out in a warm oven for several hours before eating. This makes all nuts more palatable and easier to digest.

Legumes are best eaten with an ample daily serving of a dark-green leafy vegetable such as spinach, kale or cabbage.

The protein element of your daily food could – if you are not vegan – be obtained from eggs and dairy products provided these are from animals that are kept in natural conditions, are fed a healthy, organic, drug-free and hormone-free diet and are well treated.

If your definition of vegetarianism extends to eating fish then this, of course, opens up a whole range of protein-rich choices for you.

Desserts are ideally fresh, or frozen, berries eaten with a sprinkling of ground almonds or ground pumpkin seeds and with full-fat yoghurt, or a soft goats' cheese if you are dairy tolerant. Coconut yoghurt is a good alternative.

We would advise you to avoid poor quality bread, white rice and pasta and swap them for nutritionally improved choices (see Swapping old for new on page 56 for suggestions). Consider reducing the amount of root vegetables, such as white potatoes, carrots and parsnips, you eat as they are rich in natural sugars and choose green vegetables instead. (If you eat carrots raw the available sugar is much less.)

Some adjustments to your vegetarian way of eating may be required to encourage you to incorporate more varied and nutritious meals and snacks instead of defaulting to toast or sandwiches.

Although they are vegetarian, avoid the addictive mix of carbs and vegetable fat found in corn chips, potato crisps, pretzels, crackers or popcorn. Instead, substitute with snacking on raw vegetables and homemade dips, such as pesto or humus.

If you want to reduce your portion-size of a root-vegetable-based casserole or soup, try serving it in a smaller bowl and eat it with a side salad with a virgin olive oil-based dressing. You can do the same with legumes or bean pots too.

You may find that as you increase your healthy fat intake with some nuts and avocados this helps with feelings of satiety, letting you feel fuller for longer. Make sure you use good quality cold-pressed oils, such as olive, pumpkin or avocado, to drizzle over cooked foods or salads.

Support yourself during change

You may already be one of those people who knows what to eat and understands what they need to do to achieve optimum health, including how to shed those extra pounds if appropriate. You may also be one of those people who find it challenging to commit to eating healthily without sabotaging yourself with late-night binges, sugar cravings or poor food choices. If that is the case, then perhaps there is something else happening emotionally that is blocking your ability to truly thrive.

We have worked with thousands of clients the world over wanting to free themselves from their old destructive habits around food. As therapists specialising in resolving issues around emotional eating, our first book *Seven Simple Steps to Stop Emotional Eating* (Hammersmith Books, 2015) is a guided self-help book with easy-to-learn therapy tools to help you remove the stumbling blocks to achieving your own health goals. You can find out more at www.hammersmithbooks.co.uk.

References

Academic Earth (2015) How the end of World War II made us fat. http://academicearth.org/electives/how-the-end-of-world-war-ii-made-us-fat/ (Accessed 18 July 2016)

Akbaraly TN, Brunner EJ, Ferrie JE, Marmot MG, Kivimaki M, Singh-Manoux A (2009) Dietary pattern and depressive symptoms in middle age. *British Journal of Psychiatry* 195(5): 408-413. DOI: 10.1192/bjp.bp.108.058925 http://bjp.rcpsych.org/content/195/5/408.full.pdf+html (Accessed 18 July 2016)

Batmanghelidj F (2008) *Your body's many cries for water* 3rd edition. Global Health Solutions.

Centers for Disease Control and Prevention. National Diabetes Statistics Report: Estimates of Diabetes and Its Burden in the United States, 2014. Atlanta, GA: U.S. Department of Health and Human Services; 2014 http://www.cdc.gov/diabetes/data/statistics/2014statisticsreport.html

Chowdhury EA, Richardson JD, Holman GD, Tsintzas K, Thompson D, Betts JA (2016) The causal role of breakfast in energy balance and health: a randomized controlled trial in obese adults. *American Journal of Clinical Nutrition* 103: 747-756. First published online 10 February 2016. DOI:10.3945/ajcn.115.122044

Cohen R (2013) Sugar: why we can't resist it. *National Geographic Magazine* August 2013, page 96.

Compassion in World Farming (2012) Farm assurance schemes and animal welfare – how the standards compare. 1 July. http://www.ciwf.org.uk/research/food-and-human-health/standards-analysis-report/ (Accessed 9 August 2016)

Consensus Action on Salt & Health (2015) 'Posh' salt health claims should be taken with a grain of salt! 15 November.

http://www.actiononsalt.org.uk/news/surveys/2011/gourmet%20
salts/59309.html (Accessed 9 August 2016)

Davis W (2011) Who is Dr William Davis and why is he saying such nasty
things about 'healthy whole grains'?
http://www.wheatbellyblog.com/2011/07/who-is-dr-william-davis/
(Accessed 19 July 2016)

Desideri G et al (2012) Benefits in cognitive function, blood pressure
and insulin resistance through cocoa flavanol consumption in elderly
subjects with mild cognitive impairment: The cocoa, cognition and
aging (CoCoA) study. *Hyptertension* 60: 794-801. DOI: 10.1161/
HYPERTENSIONAHA.112.193060

Diabetes UK (2016) Diabetes prevalence 2015.
https://www.diabetes.org.uk/About_us/What-we-say/Statistics/2015-as-
published-2016/ (Accessed 18 July 2016)

Eat right pro (2016) Meet our sponsors, Academy of Nutrition and Dietetics
http://www.eatrightpro.org/resources/about-us/advertising-and-
sponsorship/meet-our-sponsors (Accessed 18 July 2016)

Flegal KM, Ket BK, Orpana H, Grubard BI. Association of All-Cause Mortality
With Overweight and Obesity Using Standard Body Mass Index Categories:
A Systematic Review and Meta-analysis. *Journal of the American Medical
Association* 2013; 309(1): 71-82. DOI:10.1001/jama.2012.113905
http://jama.jamanetwork.com/article.aspx?articleid=1555137

Funk JL, Frye JB, Kuscuoglu N, et al (2006) Efficacy and mechanism of action
of turmeric supplements in the treatment of experimental arthritis. *Arthritis
Rheum* 54(11): 3452-64. DOI: 10.1002/art.22180

GB HealthWatch (2016) Omega-3:omega-6 balance.
www.gbhealthwatch.com/Science-Omega3-Omega6.php (Accessed 18 July 2016)

Gerbault P, Liebert A, Itan Y, et al (2011) Evolution of lactase persistence: an example of human niche construction. *Philosophical Transactions of the Royal Society* 366(1566): 863-877.

Hall H (2015) Intermittent fasting. *Science Based Medicine* 15 December 2015 https://www.sciencebasedmedicine.org/intermittent-fasting/ Accessed 18 July 2016.

Horwitz RJ citation to the American Academy of Pain Management: Funk JL, et al (2006) Efficacy and mechanism of action of turmeric supplements in the treatment of experimental arthritis. *Arthritis Rheum* 54(11): 3452-3464.

Malhotra A (2016) 'Why I want to drop dead healthy – and I probably will': Cardiologist says the key to a long life is ditching SUGAR – and claims he'll outlive many of today's children. *Hippocratic Post* 9 March 2016.

Mann T, Tomiyana AJ, Westling E, et al (2007) Medicare's search for effective obesity treatments: Diets are not the answer. *American Psychologist* 62(3):220-233. DOI:org/10.1037/0003-066X.62.3.220.

Mattson MP et al (2014) Meal frequency and timing in health and disease. *Proceedings of the National Academy of Sciences of the United States of America* 1111 (47): 16647-16653. DOI: 10.1073/pnas.1413965111

NACIS (2016) IBISWorld report [Weight Loss Services Market Research Report/NAICS 81219a/Feb 2016]

NHS (2016) The EatWell Guide, NHS http://www.nhs.uk/Livewell/Goodfood/Pages/the-eatwell-guide.aspx

NHS Choices (2015) Why is fibre important? http://www.nhs.uk/chq/pages/1141.aspx?categoryid=51 (last updated 5 March 2016; accessed 19 July 2016)

Observer Food Monthly's expert team (2010) The 50 Best Cookbooks of All Time. *Observer Magazine* 15 August 2010.

Public Health England (2016) Eatwell Guide. Crown copyright. https://www.gov.uk/government/uploads/system/uploads/attachment_data/file/528193/Eatwell_guide_colour.pdf Accessed 19 July 2016.

Ramsden CE, Zamora D, Majchizak-Hong S et al (2016) Re-evaluation of the traditional diet-heart hypothesis: analysis of recovered data from Minnesota Coronary Experiment (1968-73). *British Medical Journal* 353: i1246. DOI: http://dx.doi.org/10.1136/bmj.i1246

Rayner J (2015) The happy eater. *The Observer Food Magazine* 19 July.

Sathyanarayana Rao TS, Asha MR, Ramesh BN, Jagannatha Rao KS (2008) Understanding nutrition, depression and mental illnesses. *Indian Journal of Psychiatry* 50(2): 77-82. http://www.ncbi.nlm.nih.gov/pmc/articles/PMC2738337/ (Accessed 18 July 2016)

Thomas EL, Fitzpatrick JA, Malik SJ, Taylor-Robinson SD, Bell JD (2013) Whole body fat: content and distribution. *Progress in Nuclear Magnetic Resonance Spectroscopy* 73: 58-80.

Varady KA, Hellerstein MK (2007) Alternate-day fasting and chronic disease prevention: a review of human and animal trials. *American Journal of Clinical Nutrition* 86(1): 7-13.

Wenk GL (2010) *Your Brain on Food*. Oxford, UK: Oxford University Press.

World Action on Salt *&* Health (2016) Salt and your health. http://www.worldactiononsalt.com/salthealth/factsheets/index.html (Accessed 9 August 2016)

Yang Q (2010) Gain weight by 'going diet'? Artifical sweeteners and the neurobiology of sugar cravings. Y*ale Journal of Biology and Medicine* 83(2): 101-108.

Yang Q, Zhang Z, Gregg EW, Flanders WD, Merritt R (2014) Added sugar intake and cardiovascular diseases mortality among US adults. *Journal for American Medical Association – Internal Medicine* 174(4): 516-524 DOI: 10.1001/jamainternmed.2013.13563

Bibliography

As well as supporting aspects of *How to Feel Differently about Food* (see References), the books below are all valuable as further reading:

Your Body's Many Cries for Water by Dr F Batmanghelidj
First published in the early 1990s, Dr. Batmanghelidj's revolutionary book explains how if we drank more water the common degenerative diseases, such as asthma, diabetes, obesity, high blood pressure, heart disease, bulimia, Alzheimer's disease and many other afflictions, could be prevented, and sometimes cured.

Other books by the prolific doctor include *Water & Salt: Your healers within*, and *Water Cures, Drugs Kill: How Water Cures Incurable Diseases*.

Low Carb Revolution: Comfort Eating for Good Health by Annie Bell
Cutting down on carbohydrates is at the heart of eating paleo, and is not only proven as an effective way of shedding unwanted pounds, but has also been shown to have many other health benefits too. This award-winning food writer approaches low-carb eating as a food lover, and is a passionate and inspirational cook.

What to Eat by Joanna Blythman
An encyclopaedia of facts and common sense from one of the most sensible food and nutrition spokes-people of our age. She cuts through the jargon and media hype with practical and positive solutions to all our food dilemmas.

The Glucose Revolution and *The Glucose Revolution Life Plan* by Dr Jenny Brand-Miller, Kaye Foster-Powell and Johanna Burani
The definitive guide to the best foods to eat to comply with the health benefits of eating foods low on the glycaemic index (GI) scale is found in these two titles. It includes shopping lists, comprehensive store cupboard suggestions for the foods to have on hand, and easy-to-prepare recipes for many low-GI meals designed to stabilise blood sugar levels and avoid, or help reverse, the symptoms of diabetes. Also includes GI values for hundreds of foods and beverages.

How I gave up my low- fat diet and lost 40 lbs: The ultimate guide to low-carbohydrate dieting and *Paleo/Primal in 5 ingredients or less: 200 sugar-free, grain-free and gluten-free recipes* by Dana Carpender
First published in 2003, Carpender has been low-carbing for a long time and was one of the first writers we found who questioned the whole low-fat regime for weight loss that the NHS (UK National Health Service) and other countries' health services continue to promote in their national campaigns. She is also the author of countless recipe books, including her recently published title that promotes the benefits of Paleo/Primal eating.

Syndrome X: The Complete Nutritional Program to Prevent and Reverse Insulin Resistance by J Challem, Burton Berkson, Melissa Diane Smith
Syndrome X is another name for insulin resistance – the precursor to type 2 diabetes. It causes premature ageing and significantly increases the risk of heart disease, hypertension, obesity and other age-related diseases. This book outlines a three-step programme, including easy-to-follow food plans designed to safeguard you against developing syndrome X, or reverse the symptoms it if you already have it.

The Paleo Diet by Dr L Cordain
Dr Loren Cordain is the world's leading expert on Paleolithic eating. His bestselling nutrition programme is based on eating the foods we were genetically designed to eat, and features dozens of new recipes plus the latest information drawn from ground-breaking nutritional research to jump-start a healthy, and enjoyable new way of eating.

Wheat Belly by Dr William Davis
This book explores the positive repercussions to your health of eliminating wheat from your diet. They range from weight loss to improved digestion, reduction in inflammation and reduced rheumatoid arthritis pain. Davis draws on clinical experience of putting thousands of his patients on wheat-free regimens and observing the significant benefits.

Protein Power by Drs Michael and Mary Eades
This is a lifestyle plan which shows you how to use food as a tool for weight loss, resetting your metabolism, lowering bad cholesterol and protecting you

from problems such as high blood pressure and heart disease. Following their plan you can still eat the foods you love, including steaks and burgers, cheese and eggs – because this eating plan rethinks the current wisdom on fat intake versus fat-inducing carbohydrates like breads and pastas.

Go Paleo? by Eve Gilmore
Naturopathic health practitioner Eve Gilmore examines the pros and cons of going paleo and is it good for us? Is it possible in the 21st century? Is it sustainable? Thought-provoking and informative, but highly readable, this book will appeal to all those interested in discovering what really constitutes healthy eating and why it may be worth following a Stone Age diet.

Urban Caveman – Paleo-inspired recipes for the 21st century by Eve Gilmore
Eve shares over 300 original recipes, tried and tested by her many clients, that follow paleo principles and yet satisfy our contemporary cravings for comfort foods and complex flavours – a must for anyone seeking to improve their health through diet.

Eat Fat, Get Thin! and *Trick and Treat – how 'healthy eating' is making us ill* and *Natural Health and Weight Loss* by Barry Groves
The late Barry Groves was Britain's leading exponent of the low-carb way of life having lived according to its principles since the early 1960s. He was wonderfully generous with his knowledge both in person and in his writing and was a true revolutionary in the field of nutrition, ever questioning conventional wisdom on nutrition and health.

It Starts with Food: Discover the Whole 30 by Dallas & Melissa Hartwig
A 30-day nutritional reset. Based on scientific research, they provide everything you need in their detailed plan to transform your life in unexpected ways, including improvements with sleep, weight loss and an enhanced quality of life that goes on to be sustainable well beyond the initial 30 days as a way of living and eating.

Fat Chance – The hidden truth about sugar, obesity and disease by Dr Robert Lustig
Our modern Western diet is packed with hidden sugars in processed foods, drinks and even unlikely savoury foods. It is responsible for our ever-

expanding waistlines, soaring levels of diabetes and a catalogue of diseases reaching epidemic proportions. Lustig will radically alter how you see the food on your plate to aid weight loss, improve nutrition and potentially increase health and wellbeing.

Sugar Nation by Jeff O'Connell
Read and be prepared to be outraged as O'Connell sheds light on the hidden truth behind America's deadliest habit, and where America leads you know the rest of the world follows. This is a must-read for anyone who cares about what they eat and the covert policies of food manufacturing giants.

Grain Brain: The Surprising Truth about Wheat, Carbs, and Sugar – Your Brain's Silent Killers and *Brain Maker: The Power of Gut Microbes to Heal and Protect Your Brain – for Life* by Professor David Perlmutter
Renowned neurologist David Perlmutter explains how gluten and carbohydrates are destroying the brain. And not just simple carbs, but even healthy, complex carbs, such as whole grains, can cause dementia, ADHD, anxiety, chronic headaches, depression, and much more. In *Brain Maker*, Perlmutter explores the connection between intestinal microbes and the brain, describing how the microbiome develops in the gut from birth. How it evolves is based on the environment, which can lead to a healthy microbiome or poor gut health. He details how nurturing gut health through a few easy strategies can open the door to unprecedented brain health potential.

In Defense of Food and *Food Rules: An Eater's Manual* by Michael Pollan
Famous for saying 'Eat food. Not much. Mostly plants', Pollan is a captivating, and passionate writer on his chosen theme of celebrating good, honest, simple food. His books are an invitation to ignore all the nutritional conflicting advice and mumbo-jumbo from so-called experts, and instead implores us to just eat the kinds of foods our great-grandmother would have recognised.

In *Food Rules*, Pollan has written a no-nonsense pocket-size guide for anyone who wants to be more informed and mindful of what they buy at a supermarket, or eat at a restaurant or an all-you-can-eat buffet. Knowledge is power.

The Diet Delusion by Gary Taubes
Bad science and vested interests from the food giants mean we have been ill-advised and ill-informed about food and nutrition to the detriment of our health and our waistlines. Taubes provides an in-depth, ground-breaking examination of what actually happens in our bodies as a result of what we eat, including why we get fat and sick and how to prevent or correct those outcomes.

New Atkins For a New You: The Ultimate Diet for Shedding Weight and Feeling Great by Dr E Westman, Dr J Volek and Dr S Phinney
There are plenty of 'new' versions of the Atkins diet out there but this is the definitive one. Although discredited in more recent years, the Atkins diet remains the most medically researched and assessed diet ever and has proven successful for hundreds of thousands of people. The three doctors involved have made the plan more flexible and easy to follow for busy lifestyles. We think it still has a lot to offer if you want to explore the benefits of following a diet plan.

The Wahls Protocol: How I beat progressive MS using Paleo Principles and functional medicine by Dr Terry Wahls
A personal and astonishing testament that proves the wisdom of Hippocrates when he said, 'Let food be thy medicine'. Supported with medical research, this book is essential reading for not just anyone facing auto-immune disease but for everyone who wants to achieve maximum health and wellbeing.

Resources

Specialist suppliers

An up-to-date listing of specialist suppliers is available online at www.feeldifferently.co.uk – Click on 'Suppliers'.

It is particularly useful for sourcing small producers of grass-fed meat or organic produce who sell direct to the public. The prices they offer, even when deducting for delivery charges, are often cheaper than buying the equivalent organic or high welfare produce available in the high street.

The listing also includes other specialists we have come across, including people delivering real-food workshops and training sessions both live and online.

Food and mood diary

To download the A4 printer-friendly PDF version of the 'food and mood diary' template go to www.feeldifferently.co.uk and click on Therapy Tools see Worksheets tab.

Most people's memory is not accurate when tracking food they have eaten. It's human nature to underestimate portion size or simply forget about snacks or drinks grabbed on the run during the day.

Keeping a food diary at the outset of changes to your eating patterns is a positive and illustrative move that will help you as you learn what foods best suit you. The food diary we have devised also includes a way of logging moods so that you can begin to explore the link between what you eat and how you feel emotionally.

Food & Mood Diary

Name...Week beginning...................Week Number...........

Draw a circle around your hunger level each time you eat from 0 to 10 (0 not hungry at all and 10 ravenously hungry).
Take a moment to become aware of what is happening to your mood around food.

As well as noting down what you eat, make a note of how you are feeling in yourself to build a connection between what you eat and how you feel.

Day	Morning	Afternoon	Evening
	0 1 2 3 4 5 6 7 8 9 10 mood/feeling	0 1 2 3 4 5 6 7 8 9 10 mood/feeling	0 1 2 3 4 5 6 7 8 9 10 mood/feeling
	0 1 2 3 4 5 6 7 8 9 10 mood/feeling	0 1 2 3 4 5 6 7 8 9 10 mood/feeling	0 1 2 3 4 5 6 7 8 9 10 mood/feeling
	0 1 2 3 4 5 6 7 8 9 10 mood/feeling	0 1 2 3 4 5 6 7 8 9 10 mood/feeling	0 1 2 3 4 5 6 7 8 9 10 mood/feeling

Food & Mood Diary

HOW TO FEEL DIFFERENTLY ABOUT FOOD

Day	Morning	Afternoon	Evening
	0 1 2 3 4 5 6 7 8 9 10 mood/feeling	0 1 2 3 4 5 6 7 8 9 10 mood/feeling	0 1 2 3 4 5 6 7 8 9 10 mood/feeling
	0 1 2 3 4 5 6 7 8 9 10 mood/feeling	0 1 2 3 4 5 6 7 8 9 10 mood/feeling	0 1 2 3 4 5 6 7 8 9 10 mood/feeling
	0 1 2 3 4 5 6 7 8 9 10 mood/feeling	0 1 2 3 4 5 6 7 8 9 10 mood/feeling	0 1 2 3 4 5 6 7 8 9 10 mood/feeling
	0 1 2 3 4 5 6 7 8 9 10 mood/feeling	0 1 2 3 4 5 6 7 8 9 10 mood/feeling	0 1 2 3 4 5 6 7 8 9 10 mood/feeling

© Sally Baker and Liz Hogon

Index

Note: references in bold are to text describing the content in recommended further reading

Note: references in bold are to text describing the content in recommended further reading

Note: references in bold are to text describing the content in recommended further reading

Note: references in bold are to text describing the content in recommended further reading

Also by Sally Baker and Liz Hogon...

A practical guide to understanding the emotional reasons for overeating and how to overcome these, based on Sally and Liz's training and extensive experience in:
- Emotional freedom technique (EFT)
- Percussive suggestion technique (PSTEC)
- Hypnotherapy
- and other related therapies.

With case histories, work sheets and step-by-step exercises integrated with free online materials.

www.your7simplesteps.com
www.hammersmithbooks.co.uk